6.95
X.

PREFACE

Our justification for a separate course in set theory, which we were called upon to organize and teach, for upper division undergraduate and beginning graduate students at Colorado State College, was based on reports of various committees devoted to the study of the undergraduate curriculum, on our own experiences in learning and teaching mathematics, and on information gained from our meetings, both formal and informal, with high school teachers of mathematics. The course was to meet three hours per week for one quarter and would consist of students who had some degree of acquaintance with the real number system and elementary real functions. For some, the course would be a prerequisite to other required courses; for others, it would be a terminal course in their program; and for both groups, it would very likely be their first exposure to modern mathematics. Also, many of our students would be high school teachers who, faced with the problem of teaching some aspects of set theory in their own classes, were returning to the campus to extend their knowledge of the subject matter.

Although various courses in modern mathematics can be, and are, used to meet the above requirements, none, we felt, could be more basic than set theory, which occurs in one form or another in all modern subject matter in mathematics. A course designed to meet the needs of such a varied group of students as we have described must contain certain obvious ingredients. If it is to serve as a prerequisite to other courses, it should provide specific tools and techniques which the student may have occasion to employ in later applications. In this regard, special emphasis on the concept of function and related topics seemed appropriate. To deserve the name modern mathematics, the course should make the reader aware of the fact that modern mathematics does not merely say old things in a new way; we felt that the concept of transfinite cardinal numbers is an excellent means (though not the only one, of course) of illustrating this point. Finally, set theory, as a central branch of mathematics with its own assumptions, is an ideal medium in which axiomatic structure and the nature of proof can be studied.

These, and other, thoughts prompted us to adopt, as our central theme for the course, the systematic development of cardinal numbers and their arithmetic in such a way that the basic tools of set theory would be developed with emphasis placed on the subject matter as a mathematical system with a logical structure. Clearly, our course would have to be more than an advanced treatment of Venn diagrams. At the same time, the background and level of our students imposed obvious limitations on the degree to which axiomatic structure could be utilized. What was needed was a semi-axiomatic treatment in which attention to assumptions and rigor is emphasized but not to the extent of seriously hampering student progress or, worse, producing a negative attitude toward modern mathematics.

A search for a suitable textbook for the course revealed that those available were generally of two types. On the one hand, there were the rather complete axiomatic treatments which required a level of sophistication beyond that of our course. At the other extreme were to be found a few materials at the introductory level, most of which were entirely too brief or elementary for our purposes. Therefore, encouraged by our students, we began duplicating our own teaching notes to fill this apparent gap. These notes evolved into the present book.

Our treatment is axiomatic but is by no means complete. We use just those axioms which we found, after class trial, to be within the grasp of our students and yet sufficient to achieve our purpose with a certain degree of rigor. When rigor has been sacrificed we have tried to be honest with the reader by pointing it out. Anyone who attempts to strike such a balance between intuition and rigor runs the risk of including too much of some things and not enough of others. We can say of the materials presented here that they have been used with varying degrees of success in several classes, some of which consisted almost entirely of high school teachers. Reactions from those students as they continue their study and teaching have been encouraging.

We make no apology for the brief, and perhaps inadequate, treatment of logic in Chapter 1. In the early versions of the manuscript it was omitted altogether. We soon found, however, that it was necessary to teach some material of this type, and we have included just that amount which we found needed in the remaining chapters. No serious attempt is made in Chapter 1 to illustrate the logical notions developed, since we are relying on the ensuing material to illustrate these ideas extensively.

After introducing the notions of sets and their operations in Chapter 2, careful attention is given to the matter of proof by means of basic theorems about sets. Functions and related topics are treated extensively in Chapter 3. As sets, they illustrate the material developed in Chapter 2 and are indispensable for the discussion of equivalence of sets which follows in Chapter 4. The pace through these chapters is necessarily slow. At times, painstaking effort is devoted to proofs, and we include details that are often left to the reader. Such slow progress, however, is not without its reward, and we have found that beginning students particularly appreciate having detailed proofs at hand to serve as models when they are called upon to construct proofs for themselves.

In Chapter 5, cardinal numbers are introduced only after fixing the notion of equivalence of sets in Chapter 4. The arithmetic of cardinal numbers is given and coordinates the efforts of all the preceding chapters. As the reader progresses through these chapters, he will find the amount of symbolism and abstractness steadily increasing. There are at least two reasons for this. In the first place, much of the power and elegance of mathematics in general, and set theory in particular, lies in its symbolism and abstractness. To present mathematics in any other way is not fair to the student and may, in fact, even create a false impression of what constitutes modern mathematics. Secondly, although we seriously attempt to maintain a somewhat elementary level, we feel compelled to raise the student's level as he progresses through his study of the material. Recognizing the risk of defeating our own purpose by including too much of the abstract, we have tried to motivate and discuss each definition and the main results before presenting them.

With the main purpose of the book accomplished in Chapter 5, we turn to a brief discussion of ordered sets and other topics in Chapter 6. The length and scope of the course prevent us from going into great detail in these matters, but we hope the treatment is adequate enough to develop insights and arouse sufficient curiosity to prompt further study on the part of the reader.

In making acknowledgments, we would like to thank first our students who suffered through the early manuscripts. High school teachers in the various classes were especially helpful in assisting us in gauging the level of treatment. We would also like to thank the Science Division of Colorado State College for assistance in providing secretarial services. Special mention should be made of Miss Joyce Ridgel and Mrs. Glen Turner for their help in typing the final manuscript. Finally, we must thank our publishers and their reviewers for their invaluable suggestions and encouragement.

PETER W. ZEHNA

ROBERT L. JOHNSON

A FOREWORD TO THE READER

The kind of mathematics included in this text may be quite different from any you have previously studied. If this is the case, then the following suggestions on how to study this material may be of help, as they have been to our own students.

We strongly urge that you memorize each definition as soon as it appears. We are not minimizing the importance of understanding, and in connection with each definition there will be examples and discussions to aid you in that understanding, but, since each topic is so dependent upon preceding ones, we have found that memorization of the definitions will speed your progress.

As each new theorem is stated, stop reading and make a real attempt to prove the theorem by yourself. You may not be successful in every case (especially in the early topics), but the attempt will aid in pointing out the importance of previous material. Then, after reading the proof given in the text, make sure that the method of proof we have used is clear. If our proof differs from your own, either show that yours is an equivalent proof or correct it.

The exercises given at the end of most of the sections are designed not only to give practice in the use of the definitions and theorems but also to give you the opportunity to do some independent thinking. Be sure to work each of these exercises carefully.

Finally, when the study of a chapter is complete, make a summary of definitions, axioms, and theorems included in that chapter and test your understanding of each by sketching proofs and giving examples. We have provided a glossary of symbols on page 173 to assist you in summarizing material and to provide for easy reference.

CONTENTS

1

INTRODUCTION AND
ELEMENTARY LOGIC

1.1 HISTORICAL REMARKS

The notion of set or collection is probably as primitive as the notion of number. In fact, as we shall see, the two are not entirely unrelated. For example, it has been said that when a child hears the word "two" he thinks of a set consisting of two objects of his experience. Hence, the idea of collecting certain objects into a single whole seems to be quite natural. To the mathematician of the twentieth century the dividends which accrue to mathematics from this simple idea are many, and one might have expected some discoveries in this area centuries ago. However, it was not until the latter part of the nineteenth century that the German mathematician Georg Cantor (1845–1918) proposed the first formal treatment of sets as mathematical entities.

In his research in analysis Cantor arrived at a point where it seemed necessary to generalize the concept of number beyond the usual finite sense. He needed a concept that would introduce an actual infinity into mathematics.* As Cantor proceeded in this research he discovered that he could not only formalize the notion of infinite number but also classify various types of infinite numbers! To see how bold this gesture was in Cantor's contemporary world of mathematics, one has only to realize that no less a mathematician than Frederick Gauss (in 1831) had rejected the idea of an actual infinite, considering such an idea to be inadmissible in mathematics. Moreover, the early Greeks, and most mathematicians since their time, had felt that the concept of infinity was germane to the study of theology and philosophy, not mathematics.†

It is true that an "infinity" of sorts existed in mathematics before Cantor's work. However, this "infinity" came from a consideration of limits, the study of which was one of the central themes of the research in mathematics during the eighteenth and nineteenth centuries. For example, the expression $1/x^2$ was said to become large beyond finite bound as x was assigned smaller and smaller values. Indeed, the mathematical shorthand we use today, namely, "$\lim_{x \to 0} 1/x^2 = \infty$," reflects the acceptance of this version of an "infinity." But it was never intended that this concept introduced an actual infinite. On the contrary, the symbolism and the various phrases used, such as "$1/x^2$ becomes infinite as x approaches zero," were intended to abbreviate the precise idea that given any positive number k, it is possible to find a positive number h such that $1/x^2 > k$ whenever $0 < |x| < h$.

Granted that an actual infinite number had not been intended through the use of limits, why not admit into our number system a number which might be called "infinity" and which would have properties that might be expected of it in terms of the corresponding

---

* We are using the words "set," "finite," and "infinite" in a purely informal manner in this introduction, and we ask the reader to rely upon his intuitive understanding of these words at this point.

† Abraham A. Fraenkel, *Abstract Set Theory* (Amsterdam: Holland Publishing Company, 1961), p. 1.

limit relations?   One of the answers is that if we do so, we lose some of the valuable properties of our operations in the number system. For example, one natural property of this number "infinity" (dare we write ∞?) is that given any real number a we should have $a + \infty = \infty$.   However, one of the important properties of addition in the real number system is the cancellation law.   That is, if a, b, and c are real numbers and if $a + c = b + c$ then $a = b$. Notice that we lose this cancellation law if we include ∞ as a real number, for if we let $a = 1$, $b = 2$ and $c = \infty$, the cancellation law, if true, would show that $1 = 2$, a fact we cannot accept.

In the light of these remarks it is not too surprising that Cantor's works were not generally accepted by his contemporaries. However, as his work progressed and as other mathematicians, who had found wide application of the theory, also joined in the work, the importance of the subject became more apparent.   Subsequently, this field of study was labeled "set theory."

Ironically, about the time that Cantor's set theory began to gain acceptance, certain inconsistencies, called paradoxes, were discovered in the higher reaches of the subject.   One might think that because of the early reluctance to accept set theory these discoveries would have sounded the death knell for the subject.   However, interest in the theory had reached such a peak that other mathematicians such as Hilbert, Fraenkel, and Zermelo began a serious investigation of the reasons for these paradoxes and made several outstanding discoveries in their attempts to resolve them.   In the sixty-four years since the appearance of the first of the paradoxes, by Burali-Forti in 1897, progress has been made in resolving these issues, but at the date of this writing some are still without resolution.

1.2   THE ROLE OF SET THEORY IN MATHEMATICS

The growth of mathematics in the period from about 1900 to the present has been outstanding to say the least.   Set theory has played no minor role in the development of what we call modern mathematics and, as a matter of fact, may be said to be the basis for several of its branches. Even the paradoxes of set theory helped in the development of an area of mathematics known as foundations, wherein the axiomatic structure of all mathematics is crucially investigated. From a more direct point of view we now consider nearly every branch of mathematics to be a study of sets of objects of one kind or another. Thus, geometry is a study of sets of points; algebra deals with sets of numbers (or prototypes thereof) and operations on those sets. Analysis is mainly concerned with functions and the latter, as we shall see, are merely sets of a particular kind. We recognize the theory of sets as a unifier and simplifier in present-day mathematics. It is a unifier in that the language and properties of sets are extensively used in diverse branches of mathematics; it serves as a simplifier in that sets, by their very nature, treat collections of objects as entities in themselves and hence provide a convenient notation for handling those entities.

On the other hand, set theory may be viewed as a branch of mathematics having its own particular assumptions and structure. As such it deserves study for its own sake. In fact, in answer to the question which is so often posed by the student as to why set theory should be studied, we would say that first and foremost it is mathematics. If the reader has not already encountered a need for and use of set theory in his study of mathematics, it is unlikely that he will proceed much further without meeting that need and use. The main purpose of this book is to relate to the reader how Cantor's generalization of number, considered by many to be the most remarkable achievement of modern mathematics, can be accomplished through a study of sets and their properties.

To accomplish our avowed purpose, it will be necessary first to examine the structure of sets as mathematical objects. In this regard, there are essentially two avenues of approach. We mentioned previously that certain paradoxes in set theory arose shortly after Cantor's works were published. Some of these came about because of the highly intuitive nature of Cantor's definitions and assumptions. That is to say, when some of these assumptions were examined in detail and were made precise in an axiomatic setting, it was possible to derive contradictory statements. The attempts to remove these paradoxes gave rise to different axiomatic systems, none of which, as we have pointed out, were adequate for resolving all of the difficulties. An outgrowth of all this is that today it is fashionable to divide set theory into what is called naive or intuitive set theory and axiomatic set theory, although the dividing line be-between the two is not always clear.

It is not our intention to present purely naive set theory to the reader. In the first place, we feel that set theory is an ideal medium for illustrating the logical, deductive structure of mathematics and that this is best accomplished with the axiomatic approach. Secondly, we feel that the mathematics teacher, in order to teach set theory as well as related topics, needs a more systematic development of set theory than the naive approach affords. Although our approach will be axiomatic, the reader should be warned that there is much more to set theory than will be found here, i.e., we have selected only those assumptions which are needed to accomplish our main purpose. As a result of this selection, our system will be kept rela- tively small and we shall avoid some of the delicate issues which might otherwise make our progress much slower.

As a mathematical system, set theory shares with other systems the essential features of having certain undefined terms or primitive notions, defined terms called definitions, assumed relationships or axioms (sometimes called postulates), and derived relationships which we usually call theorems. For many years geometry was the only mathematical subject used to introduce most students to the deductive structure of mathematics prior to their work in the gradu- ate school. Lately, however, more and more textbooks in algebra and analysis have been written from a point of view that illustrates the logical, deductive nature of those subjects. If one of the ob- jectives in the study of mathematics is to understand the deductive nature of mathematics, then set theory, having fewer primitive terms and axioms, generally speaking, than the three systems mentioned above, presents a more economical means of achieving that objective.

We mentioned derived relationships or theorems as part of a mathematical system. Some of the benefit which we hope the reader will obtain from the method of presentation we have adopted will be a collection of tools and techniques which will be helpful in deriving relationships in all areas of mathematics. Now relationships cannot be arbitrarily derived, of course, so some rules must be specified for such derivation. For these rules we turn to the field of mathematical logic. Significant results in the matter of mathematical proof have been achieved within the past forty years by such men as Post, Gödel, Church, Turing, and Kleene. It might be appropriate to mention that this renewal of the study of logic in mathematics followed closely on the heels of the work of Hilbert and others who became concerned with the consistency of any mathematical system after the first contradictions arose from Cantor's naive set theory. In order to point out the salient features of proof in mathematics and in order to make the reasoning behind the methods of proof used in this work clearer, it will be advisable for us to turn our attention to these matters in the remaining sections of this chapter.

1.3 LOGICAL STATEMENTS AND VARIABLES

We shall not take the time to examine the various principles of logic in any great detail, and if the reader should feel uneasy about certain points because of the brief treatment given here, we entrust to him the responsibility of examining the details at greater length. For this purpose, we highly recommend the excellent treatment given by Patrick Suppes in his recent publication cited in the bibliography.

One of the basic difficulties encountered by the beginning student of any axiomatic treatment of mathematics is the matter of mathematical proof. In a large part that difficulty stems from the fact that we must use an ordinary language which is imprecise and ambiguous to describe precise mathematical concepts in an un-ambiguous fashion. Moreover, we must be able to derive relation-ships by arguing from the known to the unknown and, again, such arguments are often made with an ordinary language. Conse-quently, our first task is to remove as much of the inherent am-biguity of our language as we can by coming to some agreement on what certain words and phrases shall mean. Then, in considering an argument which is supposed to be a proof, we must decide upon criteria for its acceptability.

When we speak in a given ordinary language we begin by using simple sentences consisting of a noun and a predicate. Of course, with increased familiarity we use compound sentences or sentences made up of several simple sentences. In our mathematical lan-guage let us agree that a *statement* will either be a simple sentence or a compound sentence made up of simple sentences. We shall denote arbitrary statements by the letters p, q, r, s, etc. Used in this sense, p, for instance, is just a place-holder which may be re-placed by statements. Here, and throughout the rest of the book, we shall use the word *variable* for any letter which is used as a place-holder for objects of some specified kind. In the present discussion, logical variables are simply place-holders for statements.

A logical variable may itself involve variables of other types. For example, suppose the variable x is a place-holder for real num-bers (we call x a *real variable* for short). Then "x is greater than zero" is a simple sentence and hence a statement. If we denote this statement by the logical variable p, we see that the variable p in-volves the variable x and we may indicate this by writing $p(x)$, read "p of x."

Now when we examine statements in mathematics we will want to know when a given statement is true and when it is false. But not all statements are clearly true or false. For example, the state-ment $p(x)$ given above is neither true nor false, for until someone gives us a replacement for x from the real numbers we cannot say whether x is or is not greater than zero. However, once all variables in a given statement have been replaced by permissible objects, we should be able to decide whether the statement is true or false. Also, the truth or falsity of statements which are compound sentences should depend on the truth or falsity of its constituent simple sentences. Exactly how this dependence comes about will be reflected by agreements concerning the connectives involved in the compound statement. We shall consider these matters in the next section.

Generally speaking, when two statements are denoted by different variables, such as p and q, we shall assume that the statements are different (or distinct). When this is not the case, that is when p and q denote exactly the same statement, then we will write $p = q$. In this sense, and throughout the remainder of the book (unless otherwise specified) equality will be used as identity.

Often a general statement like $p(x)$ is made more specific by prefixing phrases like, "for every x," "for all x," "for some x," and "there exists an x such that." The symbol $\bigvee$, called the *universal quantifier*, is an abbreviation for the words "for every" or "for all." The symbol $\exists$, called the *existential quantifier*, is an abbreviation for the words "there exists." Incidentally, we find it convenient to use the symbol $\ni$, a Greek epsilon written backwards, for the words "such that." Thus, if we have the statement $p(x)$ given, we may form new statements by means of the prefixed quantifiers. For example: $q(x) = \bigvee x, p(x)$ is read "for every x, p of x" and $r(x) = \exists x \ni p(x)$ is read "there exists an x such that p of x."* Of course, if statements such as $q(x)$ and $r(x)$ are to be meaningful, there must be some agreement, tacit or otherwise, as to what kinds of objects may replace the variable x. Moreover, the decision as to whether such a statement is true or false will also depend on what kinds of objects can be used as replacements for the variable(s) in the state-

---

* The symbol $\ni$ is usually omitted in mathematical logic, and as the student becomes more familiar with the notion he may wish to drop it. However, we have observed that students find it easier if their attention is directed to the phrase "such that" by the use of the symbol and there is no harm in using it.

ment.   Let us illustrate these two points by considering the following statement:

$$s(x) = \exists\, x \ni x^2 < 0$$

If x is to be replaced only by names of certain milch cows in Wis-
consin, then it is clear that the statement is *meaningless*.   On the
other hand, if x is a real variable, then the statement is meaningful,
though false.   Finally, if we allow x to be replaced by certain complex numbers, then the statement is meaningful and true.

1.4   SENTENTIAL CONNECTIVES AND TRUTH TABLES

We come now to the matter of deciding how to form new statements from old and how to determine when such a statement is true
or false.   We may occasionally appeal to the intuition of the reader
in a few matters.

If p is a statement, one of the simplest statements we may
form from p is the *negation* of p, denoted $-p$ and read "not p."
Thus, if p is the statement "x is 3," then the negation of p is the
statement "x is not 3," i.e., $-p = (x$ is not 3$)$.   The negation of
statements involving quantifiers is slightly more tedious and perhaps not too obvious.   Rather than become involved in a lengthy
discussion, we define the negations for such statements as:

$$\text{If } p(x) = \forall\, x, q(x), \quad \text{then } -p(x) = \exists\, x \ni -q(x)$$
$$\text{If } r(x) = \exists\, x \ni s(x), \quad \text{then } -r(x) = \forall\, x, -s(x)$$

If p is an arbitrary statement, what can be said about the truth
of $-p$?   In the remarks that follow let us assume that p is meaningful and is either true or false.   Furthermore, let us denote these
two conditions by arbitrarily assigning to p the letter T when p is
true and the letter F when p is false, calling these the *truth values*

of p. We now call upon the intuition of the reader and ask that
he agree with us that when p is true, $-p$ should be false and when
p is false, $-p$ should be true. The sole reason for calling upon
intuition is to make the definition seem reasonable. At any rate,
we will use this as our definition of negation. Using our agreement
on the use of the letters T and F, we may display our definition of
negation schematically in a convenient form known as a *truth table*
in which one may see at a glance the truth value of $-p$ and its
dependence on p by reading horizontally.

p	$-p$
T	F
F	T

TABLE 1.1 • Truth table for $-p$

Before leaving the concept of negation, notice that when p and q are
distinct, we write $-(p = q)$ as $p \neq q$.

If p and q are meaningful statements, as indeed we shall consider them to be from this point on, and if p is distinct from q, there
are four possible pairs of truth values for p and q. We display
these below.

p	q
T	T
T	F
F	T
F	F

TABLE 1.2 • Possible truth values for distinct statements p and q

It is clear from our definition of equality that if $p = q$ then p and q
must have exactly the same truth value, i.e., if p is T, so is q and
if p is F, so is q.

Let p and q be statements and let us form a new statement by
means of the connective "and" which we symbolize by $\wedge$ and call

conjunction. Thus $p \wedge q$ is the statement "p and q" and is called the conjunction of p and q. As a statement, $p \wedge q$ may be true or false, and we again call upon the reader's intuition to agree with us on the following definition. $p \wedge q$ will be true when both p and q are true; otherwise, it will be assumed to be false. No difficulty should arise here since these assumptions coincide with what we expect from the ordinary use of "and." We summarize these assumptions in the truth table below.

p	q	$p \wedge q$
T	T	T
T	F	F
F	T	F
F	F	F

TABLE 1.3 • Truth table for $p \wedge q$

Not quite so simple is the matter of using the connective "or." The trouble arises from the fact that we often use "or" in two different senses. Thus, in the statement, "John passed the course or he failed it," we are using "or" in an exclusive sense whereby we assume that John cannot both pass and fail. But in the statement, "It is raining or the sun is shining," we allow the situation when both phenomena occur, and in this statement we are using "or" in a non-exclusive or inclusive sense, something like the legal and/or.*

Since there is an ambiguity involved in the use of "or" we must come to some agreement, and so we adopt the convention that the word "or" will be used throughout this book in the inclusive (and/or) sense, which we symbolize by $\vee$, called *disjunction.* Then, given the statements p and q, the statement "p or q" is denoted $p \vee q$ and is called the disjunction of p and q. The following truth table reflects our assumptions about the truth value of $p \vee q$ which generally agrees with our ordinary use.

* Note that although "or" in this sense includes the possibility of both, it does not require both. For example in "$x = 3$ or $x > 3$," "or" is still used in the inclusive sense though we cannot have both "$x = 3$" and "$x > 3$" as true statements.

p	q	$p \vee q$
T	T	T
T	F	T
F	T	T
F	F	F

TABLE 1.4 • Truth table for $p \vee q$

Another connective we shall be interested in is exemplified in the statement, "If the sun is shining, then Roy is fishing." That there is a single connective involved here may be made more obvious if we re-phrase the statement as, "The sun is shining implies Roy is fishing," although this is a little awkward from the point of view of ordinary usage. We symbolize the connective *implies* by $\Rightarrow$ and if p and q are statements, the statement $p \Rightarrow q$ is called an *implication* and may be read in a variety of ways such as "If p then q," "q is necessary for p," "p is sufficient for q," "p only if q," and "p implies q." The last is probably more closely allied with the symbolism than the others.

To establish the truth value of an implication we might first turn to the example given in the preceding paragraph. Suppose that the sun is shining and that Roy is fishing. Then we would undoubtedly agree that the statement is true, whereas we would also agree that if the sun is shining and Roy is not fishing then the statement is false. But what if the sun is not shining? Since the statement did not assert anything about Roy's behavior in this case, we might say it is natural to assume that the statement is true. Someone might equally well argue, however, that this is cause for calling it false.

Consider the mathematical example, "If $1 = 2$, then $2 = 3$." The implication here is a true one since if we must start with $1 = 2$ then, by applying some simple rules of arithmetic, we may conclude that $2 = 3$. Again someone might argue that we have no right to work with an obviously false statement in the first place. But then we are confusing truth, which is relative, with meaning, which is intuitive. In the final analysis, since there is this definite possibility of ambiguity, we are forced to make an assumption. We will agree that $p \Rightarrow q$ is false only when p is true and q is false. As usual we summarize in a truth table.

p	q	$p \Rightarrow q$
T	T	T
T	F	F
F	T	T
F	F	T

TABLE 1.5 • Truth table for $p \Rightarrow q$

Many times a component statement of a compound statement is itself compound. As such, its truth value may not be arbitrarily assigned but will depend upon the truth values of its component statements, some of which may again be compound. Ultimately, however, this dependence reduces to the truth values of statements which are no longer compound, i.e., involve no connectives at all. Let us agree to call a statement *prime* if it contains no connectives. It is then possible to find the truth value of any statement by starting with the arbitrarily assigned truth values of its prime statements, grouping statements by means of brackets and parentheses to indicate which connectives are dominant, and using only the four truth tables given above. The resulting device is called a *derived truth table*.

We will illustrate the technique of deriving a truth table with a particular conjunction which will have special significance in our work. Let p and q be prime statements and consider the compound statement, "If p then q and if q then p." Fundamentally, this compound statement is a conjunction and its component statements are implications. To denote the statement symbolically, we will need to use parentheses as follows, $(p \Rightarrow q) \wedge (q \Rightarrow p)$. The basic idea of the derived truth table is to begin with truth values of p and q and, using our tables given above, list the corresponding truth values of $p \Rightarrow q$ and $q \Rightarrow p$, respectively, finally using the appropriate table to find the truth value of the conjunction of the latter statements. The scheme given below should make this technique clear.

p	q	$p \Rightarrow q$	$q \Rightarrow p$	$(p \Rightarrow q) \wedge (q \Rightarrow p)$
T	T	T	T	T
T	F	F	T	F
F	T	T	F	F
F	F	T	T	T

TABLE 1.6 • Derived truth table for $(p \Rightarrow q) \wedge (q \Rightarrow p)$

If we compare the last column in Table 1.6 with the first two columns we notice that the compound statement $(p \Rightarrow q) \wedge (q \Rightarrow p)$ is true only when p and q have the same truth value. This fact becomes important enough to single out this particular statement as a relationship between p and q and give it a special name and symbol. First, we abbreviate the phrase "If p then q and if q then p" by the phrase "p if and only if q." Then we denote the phrase "if and only if" by the symbol $\Leftrightarrow$ called *equivalence* or *biconditional*. Finally, we define $p \Leftrightarrow q = (p \Rightarrow q) \wedge (q \Rightarrow p)$. It then becomes convenient, though not necessary, to summarize the above truth table as follows, showing the dependence of the truth value of $p \Leftrightarrow q$ on the truth values of p and q alone.

p	q	$p \Leftrightarrow q$
T	T	T
T	F	F
F	T	F
F	F	T

TABLE 1.7 • Truth table for $p \Leftrightarrow q$

As another example, which will serve as a model for deriving truth tables, we derive the truth table for the statement $[(p \vee q) \wedge r] \Rightarrow (-q \wedge p)$, where p, q, and r are prime statements.

Observe that in this case there are three prime statements and hence eight different ways of independently assigning T and F to these statements. With n prime statements it is clear that we would need 2^n rows in the derived truth table, which somewhat limits its usefulness except for the fact that we will seldom encounter cases where $n > 3$.

p	q	r	p ∨ q	(p ∨ q) ∧ r	−q	−q ∧ p	[(p ∨ q) ∧ r] ⟹ (−q ∧ p)
T	T	T	T	T	F	F	F
T	T	F	T	F	F	F	T
T	F	T	T	T	T	T	T
T	F	F	T	F	T	T	T
F	T	T	T	T	F	F	F
F	T	F	T	F	F	F	T
F	F	T	F	F	T	F	T
F	F	F	F	F	T	F	T

TABLE 1.8 • Derived truth table for $[(p \lor q) \land r] \Rightarrow (-q \land p)$

The reader will have ample opportunity to practice similar derivations in the exercises following Section 1.5, so we will not stop to introduce exercises at this point.

1.5 TAUTOLOGIES AND INFERENCE

Let us derive the truth table for the compound statement $p \lor -p$.

p	−p	p ∨ −p
T	F	T
F	T	T

TABLE 1.9 • Derived truth table for $p \lor -p$

We notice that the truth value for $p \lor -p$ is T regardless of the truth value of the prime statement p. Any statement having the property that its truth value is T for all its entries in the truth table is called a *tautology*. The importance of tautologies derives from the fact that such a statement is true regardless of the truth or falsity of its prime statements. Another example is given below.

p	q	$p \wedge q$	$q \Rightarrow (p \wedge q)$	$p \Rightarrow [q \Rightarrow (p \wedge q)]$
T	T	T	T	T
T	F	F	T	T
F	T	F	F	T
F	F	F	T	T

TABLE 1.10 • Truth table for $p \Rightarrow [q \Rightarrow (p \wedge q)]$

Given prime statements, there are many tautologies that can be constructed using connectives. Some of these are often singled out and called *laws* because of their frequent use. For example, the tautology $p \vee -p$ is called the law of the excluded middle, the name stemming from the idea that if p is any statement then either p is true or p is not true (that is, p is false) since $p \vee -p$ is always true, so that there is no "middle" possibility. Others are named in the exercises following this section.

When we reflect on the role of the logical variables in the tautologies so far considered we see that no significance was attached to the fact that we were using the particular variables p, q, etc. Indeed, a statement which is a tautology remains so when any statement is substituted for a prime statement at each occurrence of that prime statement. Observe that if any row of the truth table of a statement has the value F (i.e., the statement is false for the given truth values of the prime statements of that row), then the statement is not a tautology. Incidentally, a statement is said to be *identically false*, or is a *contradiction*, if its truth value is F for all its entries in the truth table, i.e., its negation is a tautology.

Now the reader has a right to know where all this is leading us and why we are interested in tautologies. The answer lies in the fact that one of the objectives of this chapter is the understanding of the matter of proof in mathematics, although we have no intention of examining the problem in any great detail. What we are seeking is a set of rules which will enable us to move from some given statement to some concluding statement in a step-by-step procedure which is justifiable within the framework of mathematical logic. The role played by tautologies will be more clear when we define tautological implication.

A statement p is said to *tautologically imply* a statement q if and only if the implication $p \Rightarrow q$ is a tautology. Since $p \Rightarrow q$ is false only when p is true and q is false it follows that if $p \Rightarrow q$ is a tautology, then q must be true whenever p is true. This means that the truth of q may be safely concluded from the truth of p and the fact that $p \Rightarrow q$ is a tautology.

If we are given some statement, called a *hypothesis*, and a concluding statement, which we might call the *conclusion*, and if the implication from hypothesis to conclusion is a tautology, then we call the statement consisting of hypothesis, implication, and conclusion a *theorem*. Thus, we are interested in tautologies because theorems are tautologies and theorems play a central role in mathematics.

Of course, in proving a theorem, i.e., verifying that the implication is a tautology, we sometimes do not proceed directly from the hypothesis to the conclusion but rather prove a series of intermediate theorems each leading toward the desired consequence. As a general rule we shall say that a theorem has been proved if there has been listed a sequence of statements each of which is either an axiom of the system in which we are operating, or follows tautologically from the original hypothesis of the theorem being proved. The sequence so described will be called a *valid argument*. We assume that any given hypothesis may be introduced at any step, as well as other tautologies.

We have seen that a statement p tautologically implies a statement q if and only if $p \Rightarrow q$ is a tautology. When two statements

p and q tautologically imply each other (i.e., when $p \Leftrightarrow q$ is a tautology), we will say they are *tautologically equivalent*. If $p = q$ then clearly p tautologically implies q. However, p and q may be tautologically equivalent without being identical. Nevertheless, in terms of truth values p and q play almost identical roles and for this reason give flexibility to the mathematician in his proofs. Hence, we assume that if p is tautologically equivalent to q, then p may be replaced by q wherever it occurs in a proof, without changing the validity.

In testing for tautological equivalence of two statements, it is only necessary to compare the truth values of the two statements. If the values are identical in each row, then the statements are tautologically equivalent, since the last column would contain all T's according to Table 1.5. For instance, if p and q are statements, then $p \Rightarrow q$ is tautologically equivalent to $-p \vee q$ as may be seen from the following table. Since the two columns immediately preceding the last one have the same entries row by row, it is really unnecessary to compute the last column.

p	q	$-p$	$p \Rightarrow q$	$-p \vee q$	$(p \Rightarrow q) \Leftrightarrow (-p \vee q)$
T	T	F	T	T	T
T	F	F	F	F	T
F	T	T	T	T	T
F	F	T	T	T	T

TABLE I.II • Equivalence of $p \Rightarrow q$ and $-p \vee q$

We pause now to give a set of important exercises which the reader should be certain to solve, because we will refer to the tautologies established here many times in the work which follows on set theory. Incidentally, when we refer to these exercises in the body of the text we may call them by name when appropriate or simply refer to them as Exercise 1.5–n; we will continue this practice throughout the text.

. . . .

EXERCISES

By means of derived truth tables, establish that the following are tautologies.

1. $[p \wedge (p \Rightarrow q)] \Rightarrow q$ (law of detachment)

2. $(p \wedge q) \Rightarrow p$; $(p \wedge q) \Rightarrow q$ (laws of simplification)

3. $p \Rightarrow (p \vee q)$; $q \Rightarrow (p \vee q)$ (laws of addition)

4. $[(p \Rightarrow q) \wedge (r \Rightarrow q)] \Leftrightarrow [(p \vee r) \Rightarrow q]$ (proof by cases)

5. $[(p \vee q) \wedge -p] \Rightarrow q$

6. $[(p \Rightarrow q) \wedge (p \Rightarrow -q)] \Rightarrow -p$ (law of absurdity)

7. $(p \wedge -p) \Rightarrow q$

8. $[(p \Rightarrow q) \wedge (q \Rightarrow p)] \Leftrightarrow (p \Leftrightarrow q)$

9. $p \Leftrightarrow -(-p)$ (law of double negation)

10. $(p \Rightarrow q) \Leftrightarrow (-q \Rightarrow -p)$ (law of the contrapositive)

11. $-(p \wedge q) \Leftrightarrow (-p \vee -q)$
    $-(p \vee q) \Leftrightarrow (-p \wedge -q)$ (De Morgan's laws)

12. $(p \wedge q) \Leftrightarrow (q \wedge p)$
    $(p \vee q) \Leftrightarrow (q \vee p)$ (commutative laws)

13. $[p \wedge (q \wedge r)] \Leftrightarrow [(p \wedge q) \wedge r]$
    $[p \vee (q \vee r)] \Leftrightarrow [(p \vee q) \vee r]$ (associative laws)

14. $[p \wedge (q \vee r)] \Leftrightarrow [(p \wedge q) \vee (p \wedge r)]$
    $[p \vee (q \wedge r)] \Leftrightarrow [(p \vee q) \wedge (p \vee r)]$ (distributive laws)

15. $(p \Rightarrow q) \Leftrightarrow (-p \vee q)$

16. $-(p \wedge -p)$ (law of contradiction)

17. $[(p \wedge -q) \Rightarrow (r \wedge -r)] \Leftrightarrow (p \Rightarrow q)$ (reductio ad absurdum)

18. $[(p \Rightarrow q) \wedge (q \Rightarrow r)] \Rightarrow (p \Rightarrow r)$ (transitive law)

19. $(p \Leftrightarrow q) \Leftrightarrow [(p \wedge q) \vee (-p \wedge -q)]$

20. $[(p \Rightarrow q) \wedge (p \Rightarrow r)] \Leftrightarrow [p \Rightarrow (q \wedge r)]$

1.6 PROOF IN MATHEMATICS

We conclude this chapter with a brief description of the types of proof the reader will find in this and in other mathematical texts. Our intention is to highlight the features of formal proof, informal proof, heuristic argument, as well as the difference between direct and indirect proof. We will not exhibit any examples of these proofs at this time, because we will soon illustrate each of these types in the body of the text.

A *formal proof* in mathematics consists of a sequence of statements each of which is an axiom of the mathematical system, or follows from the axioms by some tautological implication or equivalence, or is itself a tautology. Of course, the introduction of hypotheses allows further tautological implications, but the conclusion is naturally restricted to these hypotheses.

An *informal proof* in mathematics consists of just enough of the formal proof, together with appropriate remarks, to enable the reader conversant with the subject to get the gist of the formal proof. The style in which the informal proof is given is the most significant feature of such a proof and differentiates it from a formal proof. In other words, an informal proof makes apparent how the formal proof may be given but the details involved in writing out the precise logical statements are sometimes left to the reader.

A *heuristic argument* is also a very informal type of "proof" but we hesitate to use the word "proof" to describe the method. The reason for this hesitation is the fact that the argument is given from a very intuitive basis with little or no resemblance to the formal proof. For example, if the formal proof of a given theorem involves complicated algebraic manipulations, the heuristic argument given may be diagrammatical or geometric. In any case, heuristic arguments are often used to give the reader the feeling that the theorem is actually a valid one by appealing to his intuition. If the theorem is one whose formal proof is too difficult for a certain treatment, the heuristic argument is sometimes used as a substitute for a proof in order to get on with other matters. (In a lighter mood, we often speak of the heuristic argument as a "proof by coercion" since the reader is almost forced to believe the validity of the theorem.)

When a proof is presented which proceeds directly from the axioms and the hypothesis of the theorem to the conclusion by either formal or informal styles, we say that the proof given in this way is *direct*. We say that an *indirect proof* has been given when the negation of the conclusion has been used as one of the hypotheses in the proof. Some of the powerful tools that are frequently used in an indirect proof are the tautologies which we have called the law of contradiction, the law of the contrapositive, the law of absurdity, and reductio ad absurdum.

Finally, when a conclusion has been reached by formal or informal styles the reader will often see the abbreviation "Q.E.D." These letters stand for the phrase "quod erat demonstrandum" which is usually interpreted as "which was to be shown," and will be employed throughout this book to show that the proof of a theorem is ended.

Admittedly, the treatment of mathematical logic given in this chapter is brief, and the reader may feel a need for more illustrations, particularly in Section 1.6. However, to give a more comprehensive coverage of the very interesting subject of mathematical logic would delay our study of the theory of sets. Moreover, the illustrations which may be needed will be forthcoming in the main body of the text. Therefore, we turn next to the study of the theory of sets.

2

SETS AND THEIR PROPERTIES

2.1 THE UNDEFINED TERMS

We mentioned that a mathematical system must begin with undefined (primitive) terms. Let us illustrate what happens when we do not assume undefined terms but attempt to define everything. The dictionary lists almost every word in our language and "defines" these words. Suppose we examine the dictionary for a definition of the word "set" as a noun. We find something like the following:

"set: a collection or group."

Since we have not defined collection or group we return to the dictionary for definitions of these, finding a new word along the way.

"collection: a group or an assemblage."

"group: an assemblage or collection."

"assemblage: a group or collection."

It is obvious that we have no way of defining "set" from the dictionary since it is defined in terms of words which are defined in terms of each other. Such a definition is often called a *circular definition*. We avoid such a situation in set theory by choosing as undefined or primitive terms the words *set* and *element of a set*.

It is easy to gain an intuitive concept of the meaning of the word set by thinking of the familiar synonyms given above. However, as we shall see, there is more to the notion of set than can be given by these synonyms. In his early work, Cantor defined set as a collection of definite, distinguishable objects of our perception which could be conceived as a whole. Given any object whatsoever, one should be able to determine whether or not that object belongs or does not belong to a given set. Involved in Cantor's set theory is a tacit assumption regarding the existence of a set of all sets which leads to some of the paradoxes in set theory. We shall have more to say about this set in Chapter 6. Serious attempts to define set have failed, and we now generally agree that it is a primitive.

We may also form an intuitive notion of element by thinking of elements as being the objects that make up a set. Notice the error in the following attempt at definition: Set: a collection of elements; Elements: the objects which make up a set. Here is the same circular definition that we illustrated earlier in this chapter. The reader may ask, "What is a good definition?" and we answer by saying that a good definition is unambiguous, non-contradictory, uses only the terms which have been previously defined, and especially does not use the term being defined in its own definition. Incidentally, we agree that a definition is always an "if and only if" statement (i.e., a logical equivalence) whether given in that form or not.

In most of our work we shall designate a set by means of an upper-case letter. Thus, Z may represent the set of all integers, R may represent the set of all rational numbers, P the set of people who have lived in the United States from 1900 to 1950, etc. To designate the elements of a given set we shall generally use lower-case letters, and to indicate that the element a is or is not in set A we shall use the following notation:

$a \in A$, read, "a is an element of set A," and
$a \notin A$, read, "a is not an element of set A."

The diagonal slash used through a symbol will generally stand for the negation of the meaning of that symbol.

By our previous agreement in Chapter 1, that equality is used as identity, to say that set A equals set B is to say that A and B are the same set and, hence, A and B obviously have the same elements. It is very intuitively appealing to say, conversely, that if A and B have the same elements, then $A = B$. However, it is not possible to prove this statement without assuming a logically equivalent statement within the present framework. Consequently, we postulate the truth of the statement by incorporating it in our first axiom.

. . . .

AXIOM OF EXTENT

If A and B are sets, then $A = B$ if and only if every element of A is an element of B and every element of B is an element of A. Symbolically, $A = B \Leftrightarrow (x \in A \Leftrightarrow x \in B)$.

. . . .

We will often want to specify a set in a particular way. For example, let A be some set of real numbers (not necessarily all of the real numbers) and let $p(x)$ be the statement, "$x > 0$." Now if we wish to collect those elements of A which, when substituted for x in $p(x)$, make $p(x)$ a true statement, then we want the system and its notation to allow us to call the result a set. Moreover, if the statement is meaningless when its variables are replaced by any of the elements of the given set, then we want such a statement to be excluded from consideration. (Here, the word "meaningless" is being used intuitively as in Chapter 1 and is admittedly a concession in opposition to rigor.)   To ensure that we may always specify a set of elements from a given set which make some statement true, or which have a certain property, we give the second axiom of the system.

· ·

AXIOM OF SPECIFICATION

If A is a set and $p(x)$ is a meaningful statement for every x in set A, then there exists set B such that $y \in B$ if and only if $y \in A$ and $p(y)$ is true.   We write: $B = \{y; y \in A, p(y)\}$ which is read, "B equals the set of all y's such that y is an element of A and $p(y)$ is true."

· ·

The notation used to describe set B is often called the "set builder" form of set description.   Notice that the semi-colon is used for the words "such that" in this form.   We will never use the semi-colon to stand for these words except in the set builder form.   (A colon or a vertical bar are also used for this same purpose.)   It should also be noticed that the words, "and $p(y)$ is true" are abbreviated by simply writing $p(y)$.   Also, when the set A is clearly understood we often write B more briefly as $B = \{y; p(y)\}$.

The statement $p(x)$ is called the *defining property* of set B, and in this sense B is described as the set of all elements of set A which have the property $p(x)$, or, stated more simply, which have the property p.   When $p(x)$ is meaningful, as indeed it will be throughout the remainder of this text, we shall say that set B is *well-defined*. This is not an attempt to define "set" but is merely a guarantee that the set in question does exist in accordance with the axiom.

Let us consider some examples of the use of the Axiom of Specification and the set builder notation.

EXAMPLE (1)

Let Z be the set of integers and $p(x) = (x$ is less than 1000 and x is positive). Clearly, set B may be written, $B = \{y; y \in Z, 0 < y < 1000\}$.

In this example, since we are given a specific defining statement $p(x)$, we have placed an abbreviated version of $p(x)$ in the notational form of B. It would be well to mention at this point that we attach no special significance to the fact that the letter chosen for the variable in B was y. That is, B may also be written as follows:

$$B = \{z; z \in Z, 0 < z < 1000\}, \text{ or}$$
$$B = \{s; s \in Z, 0 < s < 1000\}, \text{ etc.}$$

EXAMPLE (2)

Let R be the set of rational numbers and $p(x) = (x^2 + x - 2 = 0)$. Then let $C = \{x; x \in R, x^2 + x - 2 = 0\}$.

It is clear from elementary algebra that there are two and only two elements in set C, namely 1 and -2. Thus $p(x)$ could be re-stated "x is 1 or x is -2." Hence C may be written, $C = \{x; x = 1$ or $x = -2\}$. In practice, when the number of elements in a set is small and when they have convenient names, we will simply list these names within braces and use the resulting notation as another name for the set. Thus, we write, $C = \{1, -2\}$.

EXAMPLE (3)

$D = \{0,2,4,6,8\}$. This indicates that D is the set of integers whose numerals appear within the braces. Let us compare D with the set:

$$E = \{0,2,2,4,6,6,4,8,2,0,4,6\}.$$

That $D = E$ follows from the Axiom of Extent since D and E have precisely the same elements in spite of the fact that some of the elements in E are listed more than once.

EXAMPLE (4)

Now consider the set of all fraternities on the campus of Schnellenbitte University. Suppose that the names of these fraternities are Alpha, Beta, and Gamma. Since the number of fraternities is few and have convenient names we may form the following set:

$$F = \{\text{Alpha,Beta,Gamma}\}$$

In this case F has three elements and each of these elements is a name for a set of men.

EXAMPLE (5)

$\Im = \{T; T \text{ is a triangle}, T \text{ is equilateral}\}$. The set $\Im$ has been formed from the set of all triangles and the defining statement $p(T) = T$ is equilateral. In this example, $\Im$ is a set of sets since each triangle is itself a set of points. Generally speaking, we denote sets whose elements are themselves sets by script letters.

. . . .

In the following exercises and throughout the text it will be convenient to use standard letters for some of the common sets. Let us agree to use the following scheme.

N: the set of natural numbers.

Z: the set of integers.

R: the set of rational numbers.

E_1: the set of real numbers.

C: the set of complex numbers.

. . . .

EXERCISES

1. Using your own dictionary, find one or two examples of circular definitions.

2. For each of the following sets, write a description of the set using the set builder notation from the Axiom of Specification.

$A = \{1,3\}$

$B = \{\frac{1}{5}, \frac{2}{5}, \frac{3}{5}, \frac{4}{5}, 1\}$

$C = \{\ldots, -4, -2, 0, 2, 4, \ldots\}$ (The dots indicate that the pattern is established by the elements listed and it is to be understood that the listing goes on indefinitely in this manner.)

$D = \{1, 4, 9, 16, \ldots\}$

$E = \{0, 7, 26, 63, \ldots\}$

3. For each of the following sets, write the names of the individual elements of that set within braces.

$A = \{x; x \in N, 5 < x < 8\}$

$B = \{w; w \in Z, |w| < 5\}$

$C = \{y; y \in E_1, y^2 - 5y + 2 = 0\}$

$D = \{z; z \in C, z^3 = 1\}$

4. Give an example of a set whose elements are sets having elements that are themselves sets.

5. Can you give an example of a set which contains itself as an element?

2.2 SUBSET AND OTHER DERIVED TERMS

If all of the elements of set A are elements of set B, then we say that A is a *subset* of B, or that A is *contained* in B. For example, if $B = \{x,y,z,w\}$ and $A = \{x,y\}$, then A is a subset of B. Similarly $C = \{x\}$ and $D = \{x,y,z,w\}$ are subsets of B.

. . . .

DEFINITION 2.1

A set A is a *subset* of set B, denoted $A \subseteq B$, if and only if each element of A is an element of B. We write, $(A \subseteq B) \Leftrightarrow (x \in A \Rightarrow x \in B)$, giving the symbolic counterpart of the worded definition, a practice to be followed throughout the remainder of the book.

· ·

DEFINITION 2.2

If $A \subseteq B$, then B is called a *superset* of A.

· ·

It is clear that set A will fail to be a subset of B if there exists an element of A which is not an element of B. If A is not a subset of B, we will write, $A \nsubseteq B$, read "A is not a subset of B." Symbolically, $(A \nsubseteq B) \Leftrightarrow (\exists\ x \in A \ni x \notin B)$.

In the illustrations preceding the definitions it should be observed that set D is not only a subset of B but also equals B. On the other hand, sets A and C, though subsets, are not equal to set B. We will wish to make a distinction between these two kinds of subsets and therefore make the following definition.

· ·

DEFINITION 2.3

Set A is said to be a *proper subset* of set B, denoted $A \subset B$, if and only if $A \subseteq B$ and there exists an element of B which is not in A. We write, $(A \subset B) \Leftrightarrow (A \subseteq B$ and $\exists\ x \in B \ni x \notin A)$.

· ·

DEFINITION 2.4

Set A is said to be an *improper subset* of set B if and only if $A = B$.

· ·

Some adjustment in the reader's intuitive notion of set may now be needed, because we wish to consider a set which contains no elements. Probably the synonyms like collection and assemblage will have to be discarded at this point for we do not usually think of a collection as having nothing in it. We have seen examples of sets of this sort in elementary work such as the set of real numbers which are solutions of the equation $x^2 + 1 = 0$ or the set of integers each of which is not equal to itself.

Since each of these sets contains no elements, it follows from the Axiom of Extent that they are equal in the following way. Suppose that sets A and B contain no elements. Then the implication $x \in A \Rightarrow x \in B$ is true because $x \in A$ is false. Incidentally, we say that the implication is *vacuously satisfied* in cases like this. Also $x \in B \Rightarrow x \in A$ is true for the same reason, i.e., $x \in B$ is false. Thus, $x \in A \Leftrightarrow x \in B$ is true by conjunction so that $A = B$ by the Axiom of Extent. Therefore, there is only one set containing no elements.

. . . .

DEFINITION 2.5

The set containing no elements, denoted $\emptyset$, is called the *empty set*.

. . . .

Notice that the discussion preceding the definition permits the use of the word "the" when speaking of "the empty set" since we know that there is only one. The reader may find it convenient at later points in this text to have a means of describing the empty set in set builder form. Some possibilities are given here and there are many others.

$$\emptyset = \{x; x \neq x\}; \quad \emptyset = \{x; x \in Z, x = x + 1\}$$

A general description, coming from the law of contradiction, could also be given as follows:

$$\emptyset = \{x; p(x) \wedge -p(x)\}$$

Before stating our first theorem, observe that the statement, $(\forall q, x \in \emptyset \Rightarrow q)$ is a true implication since the hypothesis is false. Thus, the statement, "If x is an element of the empty set, then x is a white-eyed screech owl," is a true statement. Furthermore, the statement, $\forall x, x \notin \emptyset$, is also true and follows from Definition 2.5.

. . . .

THEOREM 2.1

If A is a set, then $\emptyset \subseteq A$.

PROOF

$x \in \emptyset \Rightarrow x \in A$ is a true implication by the discussion above. Hence, $\emptyset \subseteq A$ by Definition 2.1. Q.E.D.

. . . .

The proof of Theorem 2.1 given above is an example of a direct proof as discussed in Section 1.5 of Chapter 1. Let us illustrate the indirect method of proof discussed in the same section by means of an alternate proof of Theorem 2.1. Remember that an indirect proof is a proof in which the negation of the conclusion of the theorem is used as an hypothesis.

. . . .

ALTERNATE PROOF OF THEOREM 2.I

Assume $\emptyset \nsubseteq A$. Then $\exists\, x \ni x \in \emptyset$ and $x \notin A$. But $\forall\, x$, $x \notin \emptyset$. Therefore, $x \in \emptyset$ and $x \notin \emptyset$ which violates the law of contradiction. Thus, by reductio ad absurdum, $\emptyset \subseteq A$. Q.E.D.

. . . .

If $A = \{a,b\}$, let us list all of its subsets.

$$\emptyset \subseteq A,\ \{a\} \subseteq A,\ \{b\} \subseteq A,\ \{a, b\} \subseteq A$$

Hence, the set of all subsets of A is given by

$$\{\emptyset, \{a\}, \{b\}, \{a, b\}\}$$

Similarly, if $B = \{x,y,z\}$, then the set of all subsets of B is the set

$$\{\emptyset, \{x\}, \{y\}, \{z\}, \{x,y\}, \{x,z\}, \{y,z\}, \{x,y,z\}\}$$

The set of all subsets of a given set is called the *power set* of that set, and we formalize this concept in the following definition.

. . . .

DEFINITION 2.6

For every set A, the set of all subsets of A, denoted $p(A)$, is called the *power set* of A. Symbolically, $p(A) = \{B; B \subseteq A\}$.*

. . . .

As seen from the two examples above, when a set contains two elements, its power set contains four elements. If a set contains three elements its power set contains eight elements. The reader will be asked to generalize this idea and prove his assertion in the exercises at the end of this section.

In view of the definition of subset and the Axiom of Extent, we may easily prove the following important theorem.

. . . .

THEOREM 2.2

If A and B are sets, then $A = B$ if and only if $A \subseteq B$ and $B \subseteq A$.

PROOF

If $A = B$, then every element of A is an element of B and every element of B is an element of A by the Axiom of Extent, so that $A \subseteq B$ and $B \subseteq A$ by Definition 2.1.

If $A \subseteq B$ and $B \subseteq A$, then every element of A is an element of B and every element of B is an element of A by Definition 2.1. Hence, by the Axiom of Extent, $A = B$.   Q.E.D.

. . . .

The reader will find that Theorem 2.2 is extremely valuable in proving two sets equal. Outlined below is a pattern of proof illustrating the use of Theorem 2.2 to which the reader may wish to refer from time to time.

---

* In more sophisticated treatments of set theory, the question of existence of $p(A)$ is a delicate matter and is usually postulated by means of a "power axiom."

· ·

USE OF THEOREM 2.2 TO PROVE $A = B$.

PROOF

Let $x \in A$. From this some inference may usually be made, due to the nature of set A, which should ultimately lead to the conclusion that $x \in B$. Then, since x is an arbitrary element of A, conclude that every element of A is an element of B. Hence, $A \subseteq B$ by Definition 2.1.

Next, let $y \in B$. Again some inference may usually be made, due to the nature of B, which should ultimately lead to the conclusion that $y \in A$. Since y is arbitrary, every element of B is an element of A, or $B \subseteq A$ by Definition 2.1.

Finally, since $A \subseteq B$ and $B \subseteq A$, $A = B$ by Theorem 2.2.   Q.E.D.

WARNING

Do not specify x (or y) as a *particular* element of A (or B), since we want to draw a conclusion regarding *every* element of A (or B), and hence must be sure that x (or y) is arbitrary.

· ·

In this and the preceding section we have discussed equality of sets, subset, and element of a set. It is imperative that the reader pay close attention to the differences involved in these notions. Observe that set A may be a subset of set B, $A \subseteq B$, or it may happen that B consists of elements one of which is set A in which case $A \in B$. The following set of exercises should give sufficient practice in the proper use of these symbols.

· ·

EXERCISES

1. If A, B, and C are sets, prove the following.

   a. $A \subseteq A$.

   b. If $A \subseteq B$ and $B \subseteq C$, then $A \subseteq C$. (This is called the transitive property of $\subseteq$.)

   c. If $A \subseteq B$ and $B \subset C$, then $A \subset C$.

   d. If $A \subseteq B$ and $A \nsubseteq C$, then $B \nsubseteq C$.

2. In the following, decide whether the statement is true or false. If true, show why. If false, give a counter-example, i.e., an instance when the statement is false.

a. If $A \neq B$ and $B \neq C$, then $A \neq C$.
b. If $A \subseteq B$ and $B \nsubseteq C$, then $A \nsubseteq C$.
c. If $x \in B$ and $B \in C$, then $x \in C$.
d. If $A \in B$ and $B \nsubseteq C$, then $A \notin C$.

3. If A is a set prove:

$$(A \subseteq \varnothing) \Leftrightarrow (A = \varnothing)$$

4. Give two examples of each of the following:

$A \in B, A \subseteq B, A \subset B,$ and $A = B$.

5. Form the power set of a set containing four elements; five elements. How many elements are there in each of the power sets described?

6. Give a general formula for the number of elements in $p(A)$ where A contains n elements. Prove your assertion. (Hint: refer to a formula from your study of permutations and combinations in "counting" the number of subsets of various sizes.)

2.3 COMPLEMENTARY SET

Suppose we are asked to consider all those integers which are not multiples of 3. Then we think of integers like 1, 2, 4, 5, -1, -2. If we are also asked to describe the set of such numbers we may do so using the Axiom of Specification.

$$A = \{x; x \in Z, x \text{ is not a multiple of } 3\}$$

This is not a very satisfactory description however since it does little more than condense the word description symbolically and only slightly at that. It is probably easier to think first of the set of all integers which are multiples of 3. Then the set A would consist of what remains when we "remove" the multiples of 3 from Z. This suggests the following definition and provides another means of describing A.

. . . .

DEFINITION 2.7

If A and B are sets, then the set of elements in B which are not in A, denoted $B - A$ and read "B minus A," is called the *complement of A with respect to B*. Symbolically, $B - A = \{x; x \in B, x \notin A\}$.

. . . .

Thus, if T is the set of integral multiples of 3, the set A above can be described in the following way:

$$A = Z - T$$

That is, $A = \{x; x \in Z, x \notin T\}$.

Observe that if A and B are sets, then $A - B$ does not equal $B - A$ in general. If we think of complementation as an operation between two sets, then we see that it is a non-commutative operation.

In each of the following exercises, you may expect to use any of the definitions given up to this point as well as the two theorems. Each exercise has the status of a theorem but since the conclusions will be used infrequently in the material which follows, we place them here as exercises. To illustrate the use of Theorem 2.2, we shall give an example of a proof following the pattern described on page 35.

. . . .

EXAMPLE

If A is a set, then $A - \emptyset = A$.

PROOF

Let $x \in A - \emptyset$. Then $x \in A$ and $x \notin \emptyset$ by Definition 2.7. But $[(x \in A) \wedge (x \notin \emptyset)] \Rightarrow (x \in A)$ by the law of simplification. Therefore, every element of $A - \emptyset$ is an element of A, and $A - \emptyset \subseteq A$ by Definition 2.1.

Let $y \in A$. Certainly y is not in the empty set since the statement $y \notin \emptyset$ is true. Thus, $y \in A$ and $y \notin \emptyset$, or $y \in A - \emptyset$ by Definition 2.7. Therefore, every element of A is an element of $A - \emptyset$ and $A \subseteq A - \emptyset$.

Since $A - \emptyset \subseteq A$ and $A \subseteq A - \emptyset$, $A - \emptyset = A$ by Theorem 2.2.

Q.E.D.

. . . .

EXERCISES

Prove the following statements.

1. If A and B are sets, then $A - B \subseteq A$.

2. If A is a set, then $A - A = \emptyset$.

3. If A is a set, then $A - (A - \emptyset) = \emptyset$.

4. If A and B are sets and $A \subseteq B$, then $B - (B - A) = A$.

5. If A is a set, then $\emptyset - A = \emptyset$.

6. If A, B, and C are sets, then $(A - B) - C = (A - C) - (B - C)$.

7. If A and B are sets, then $A - B \neq B - A$. (Give a counterexample.)

2.4 SET UNION AND INTERSECTION

You may have seen the demonstration in elementary science which supposedly shows that "$1 + 1 = 1$." This "remarkable" fact is shown by filling a cup to the very brim with coffee. To this the demonstrator very slowly "adds" one heaping tablespoon of sugar, but no coffee runs over the lip of the cup indicating no volume change has occurred. Therefore, in volume at least, "$1 + 1 = 1$." A somewhat similar situation occurs in set theory. To the non-empty set of all women in Tombstone, Arizona, who are Daughters of the American Revolution, "add" the non-empty set of all women of Tombstone who are members of the Order of Eastern Star. The result of this "addition" is simply the same set of women in Tombstone who are Daughters of the American Revolution. Thus 1 (set) "plus" 1 (set) equals 1 (set). This striking fact is less amazing when we realize that every member of the Order of Eastern Star is also a member of the Daughters of the American Revolution.

Although the implication in both of these non-mathematical examples is that arithmetical "addition" is involved, such is not the case. There is an important mathematical aspect to the second example, however, and we continue our study of set theory with a formal definition of that aspect.

. . . .

DEFINITION 2.8

Let A and B be sets. The *union of A and B*, denoted $A \cup B$, is the set of all elements which are in set A or in set B. Symbolically, $A \cup B = \{x; (x \in A) \vee (x \in B)\}$.

. . . .

The following examples may help the reader understand the meaning of this definition.

. . . .

EXAMPLES

(1) $A = \{2,4,6,8\}$; $B = \{1,3,5\}$;
    $A \cup B = \{1,2,3,4,5,6,8\}$.

(2) $C = \{a,b,c,d\}$; $D = \{b,c,d,e\}$; $C \cup D = \{a,b,c,d,e\}$.

(3) $R = \{$Lillian,Mary,Naomi,Pearl$\}$; $S = \{$Naomi,Pearl$\}$;
    $R \cup S = \{$Lillian, Mary, Naomi, Pearl$\} = R$.

(4) $F = \{x; x \in Z, 0 < x < 5\}$; $G = \{y; y \in Z, 10 < y < 12\}$;
    $F \cup G = \{w; w \in Z, 0 < w < 5 \text{ or } 10 < w < 12\}$
    $= \{1,2,3,4,11\}$.

. . . .

It should be noted that no element is listed more than once in the union of C and D or in the union of R and S since, as we have seen, it is unnecessary to do so. Note also that the use of the word "or" agrees with the inclusive interpretation agreed upon in Chapter 1.

Often a non-empty set, say T, has the property that to each $t \in T$ there corresponds a set C_t. For example, if $T = \{a,b,c\}$ the three corresponding sets are C_a, C_b, and C_c, respectively. We say that each $t \in T$ *indexes* the sets C_t and when T is used in this way we call T an *index set*.

. . . .

DEFINITION 2.9

Let T be an index set and suppose that $\forall\, t \in T$, C_t is a set. The *union of the sets* C_t, denoted $\bigcup_{t \in T} C_t$, is the set of all elements that are in C_t for some $t \in T$. In symbols, $\bigcup_{t \in T} C_t = \{x; x \in C_t \text{ for some } t \in T\}$.

. . . .

This definition is more general than Definition 2.8, since the union of any number of sets may be found using Definition 2.9. For example, if $T = \{a,b,c,d\}$ and $C_a = \{1,2\}$, $C_b = \{1,2,3,4\}$, $C_c = \{3,4,5\}$, $C_d = \{1,3,5,7\}$, then $\bigcup_{t \in T} C_t = \{1,2,3,4,5,7\}$.

Special cases arise when the index set has a special characteristic. For instance, if $T = \{a\}$, then we agree that $\bigcup_{t \in T} C_t = C_a$. Often T is a certain subset of the natural numbers which gives rise to another special case. For example, if $T = \{1,2,3, \ldots, n\}$, we may write $\bigcup_{t \in T} C_t$ as $\bigcup_{k=1}^{n} C_k$ which is read, "The union of the sets C_k as k takes the values from 1 to n inclusive."

At a recent awards program at the University, all students who had earned a football letter were asked to come to the stage for recognition. When properly recognized and re-seated, all those students with an A average were then asked to come to the stage. Some students went to the stage on both occasions and this set of students is called the *intersection set* of the two sets of students. We formalize this in Definition 2.10.

. . . .

DEFINITION 2.10

Let A and B be sets. The *intersection of A and B*, denoted $A \cap B$, is the set of all elements which are both in A and in B. Symbolically, $A \cap B = \{x; (x \in A) \wedge (x \in B)\}$.

. . . .

Again, we offer a few examples to help clarify the meaning of the definition.

. . . .

EXAMPLES

(1) $A = \{1,2,3,4,5\}$; $B = \{1,3,5\}$; $A \cap B = \{1,3,5\}$.

(2) $C = \{a,b,c,d\}$; $D = \{c,d,e,f\}$; $C \cap D = \{c,d\}$.

(3) $P = \{\text{Jack,Frank,Roy,Pete}\}$; $Q = \{\text{Ned,Leo,Marty}\}$;
$P \cap Q = \varnothing$.

(4) $F = \{x; x \in Z, 0 < x < 5\}$; $G = \{y; y \in Z, 4 \le y < 7\}$;
$F \cap G = \{w; w \in Z, 4 \le w < 5\} = \{4\}$.

. . . .

As in the case of set union we will define a more general form of set intersection.

. . . .

DEFINITION 2.11

Let T be an index set and suppose that $\forall t \in T$, C_t is a set. The *intersection of the sets C_t*, denoted $\bigcap_{t \in T} C_t$, is the set of all elements which are in C_t for each $t \in T$. In symbols, $\bigcap_{t \in T} C_t = \{x; x \in C_t$ for each $t \in T\}$.

. . . .

If $T = \{a,b,c,d\}$, and $C_a = \{1,2,3\}$
$$C_b = \{2,3,4,5\}$$
$$C_c = \{2,3,5,7\}$$
$$C_d = \{1,2,3,5\}$$

then $\bigcap_{t \in T} C_t = \{2,3\}$. As in the case of set union we agree that if $T = \{a\}$, then $\bigcap_{t \in T} C_t = C_a$. Furthermore, if $T = \{1,2,3,\ldots,n\}$, we may write the intersection of the sets C_t as follows:

$$\bigcap_{k=1}^{n} C_k$$

When two sets have no elements in common, as in Example (3), it follows that their intersection set is empty. We will find such a situation occurring frequently and give it a special name in the next definition.

. . . .

DEFINITION 2.12

If A and B are sets and $A \cap B = \emptyset$, then A and B are called *disjoint sets* (or they are said to be *disjoint*).

. . . .

EXERCISES

The sets referred to by letter in the following exercises are those given below. (N, Z, R, E_1, and C are still used as we defined them on page 28.)

$E = \{x; x \in Z, x = 2n \text{ for some } n \in Z\}$ (the *even* integers)

$D = \{y; y \in Z, y = 2n + 1 \text{ for some } n \in Z\}$ (*odd* integers)

$P = \{w; w \in Z, 0 < w < 25 \text{ and } w \text{ is prime}\}$

$T = \{z; z \in Z, z = 3n \text{ for some } n \in Z\}$ (multiples of 3)

1. Describe the following sets using the set builder form, or list the individual elements in braces.

a. $E \cup D$ e. $P \cap D$

b. $E \cap D$ f. $(Z \cap P) \cup D$

c. $N \cap P$ g. $(N \cup E) \cap T$

d. $Z - E$ h. $(E \cap T) \cap P$

2. Compare the following pairs of sets and draw proper conclusions.

  a. $E \cap P, P \cap E$

  b. $D \cup P, P \cup D$

  c. $(N \cap E) \cap T, N \cap (E \cap T)$

  d. $(N \cup E) \cap T, (N \cup T) \cap (E \cup T)$

3. Prove: If A and B are sets, then $A \cap B \subseteq A \cup B$.

4. If $T = \{a,b,c,d\}$, $C_a = \{x,y\}$, $C_b = \{x,y,z\}$, $C_c = \{y,z,w\}$, $C_d = \{x,y,z,w\}$, find the following:

  a. $\underset{t \in T}{\bigcup} C_t$

  b. $\underset{t \in T}{\bigcap} C_t$

2.5 UNIVERSAL SETS AND VENN DIAGRAMS

In a given discussion it is often convenient to limit the topics to be discussed by means of an agenda or similar device. In set theory we may wish to limit consideration in a given discussion to sets of natural numbers, for example, and to ignore other kinds of sets simply for the purposes at hand. A set to which consideration is thus limited is called a *universe of discourse*. The words "universal set" may be found in the literature in the place of universe of discourse.

Some of the exercises in the preceding section may have suggested a few theorems to the reader. However, before we attempt to prove any of these generalizations, we will examine a device which may help to point out other generalizations and which will make many of the conclusions at least intuitively appealing.

This device is a simple diagrammatical portrayal of a universe of discourse and some of its subsets. A universe of discourse is represented by a large rectangular area and subsets within this universe are represented by circular areas. If a certain set is only partially in the universe of discourse, it may be represented by a circular area part of which is in the rectangle. Such diagrams are called *Venn diagrams* after their inventor.

For example, let *A* and *B* be subsets of a universe of discourse *U*. We may represent this fact as shown in Figure 2.1. Observe that the circular areas *A* and *B* overlap, indicating the possibility that their intersection may not be empty.

The shaded area in Figure 2.2 represents the union of *A* and

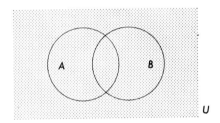

FIGURE 2.1 • Sets *A* and *B* within the universe of discourse *U*

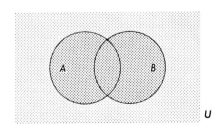

FIGURE 2.2 • $A \cup B$

B, whereas the shaded area of Figure 2.3 represents their inter-section.

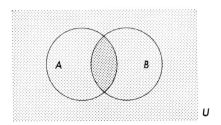

FIGURE 2.3 • $A \cap B$

In Figure 2.4 set A is represented as a subset of a universe of discourse and the shaded area represents the complement of A with respect to U, $U - A$. Figure 2.5 illustrates $U - A$ when A is not a subset of U.

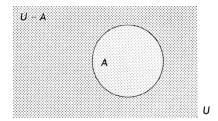

FIGURE 2.4 • $U - A$, $A \subseteq U$

Many of the theorems proved in the next section will involve three sets and the reader may want to sketch Venn diagrams for some of these theorems. Figure 2.6 shows three sets, A, B, and C, within a universe of discourse U, with $(A \cup B) \cup C$ shaded and $(A \cap B) \cap C$ a different shade. The representation of the three sets in Figure 2.6 is intended to be as arbitrary as possible with regard to intersections. Let us number each of these areas as in Figure 2.7, and briefly discuss some of the combinations. Observe that set A consists of the areas numbered 1, 2, 3, and 7. Set B consists of areas

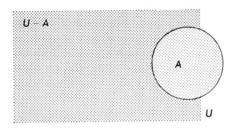

FIGURE 2.5 • $U - A, A \nsubseteq U$

3, 4, 5, and 7 and set C consists of areas 5, 6, 7, and 2. Notice that $A \cap B$ is represented by the areas numbered 3 and 7; $A \cap C$ is represented by the areas 2 and 7; $B \cup C$ is represented by the areas numbered 2, 3, 4, 5, 6, and 7; and $(A \cap B) \cap C$ is represented by the area numbered 7. Of course, given a special situation, some of these areas may be empty, but the portrayal is nonetheless effective.

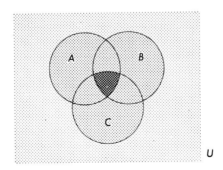

FIGURE 2.6 • Sets A, B, and C within set U, showing $(A \cup B) \cup C$
and $(A \cap B) \cap C$

For example, if $B \subseteq A$, then areas 4 and 5 are empty since every element of B is an element of A. Therefore, set B consists of areas numbered 3 and 7 in that case.

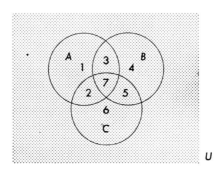

FIGURE 2.7 • Sets A, B, and C within set U with areas numbered

As an illustration of the use of Venn diagrams, let us show that the following theorem is a reasonable one by heuristic arguments based on Venn diagrams.

· ·

THEOREM

If A, B, and C are sets, then

$$A \cap (B \cup C) = (A \cap B) \cup (A \cap C)$$

HEURISTIC ARGUMENT

First, we sketch a Venn diagram of three sets and number the areas as in Figure 2.8. Next, we note that $(B \cup C)$ is represented by areas 2, 3, 4, 5, 6, 7 and that set A is represented by areas 1, 2, 3, 7. Therefore, from the definition of set intersection, $A \cap (B \cup C)$ must be represented by areas 2, 3, 7.

Now consider the set $(A \cap B) \cup (A \cap C)$. Observe that $(A \cap B)$ is represented by areas 3, 7 and $(A \cap C)$ by areas 2, 7. Therefore, from the definition of set union, $(A \cap B) \cup (A \cap C)$ must be represented by areas 2, 3, 7.

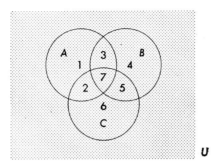

FIGURE 2.8 • Venn diagram for the theorem

Since both sets are represented by the same areas we conclude that the sets are equal.

. . . .

Another heuristic argument for the theorem may be given as follows.

. . . .

First, sketch two Venn diagrams showing three sets. Then, in the first diagram, *lightly* shade the area representing $B \cup C$. Next, shade set A *more heavily*. Now the area which is *very heavily* shaded represents the set $A \cap (B \cup C)$.

Now in the second diagram, *lightly* shade the area $(A \cap B)$ and shade the area $(A \cap C)$ *more heavily*. Then the *total* area which is shaded represents the set $(A \cap B) \cup (A \cap C)$.

Since the final areas in both diagrams are the same, we conclude that $A \cap (B \cup C) = (A \cap B) \cup (A \cap C)$.

The end result of the shading of these areas is represented in Figures 2.9 and 2.10.

. . . .

EXERCISES

Sketch Venn diagrams and give heuristic arguments which make the following statements plausible. A, B, and C are arbitrary sets.

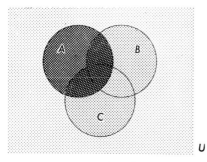

FIGURE 2.9 • $A \cap (B \cup C)$

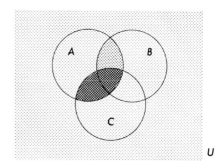

FIGURE 2.10 • $(A \cap B) \cup (A \cap C)$

1. $A \cup B = B \cup A$.
2. $A \cap B = B \cap A$.
3. $(A \cup B) \cup C = A \cup (B \cup C)$.
4. $(A \cap B) \cap C = A \cap (B \cap C)$.
5. $A \cup (B \cap C) = (A \cup B) \cap (A \cup C)$.
6. $A \cap (B - A) = \varnothing$.
7. $A \cup (B - A) = A \cup B$.

2.6 THEOREMS ON SETS

Now that some of the basic terminology of set theory has been defined and two simple theorems have been proved, we will follow a systematic procedure to establish other useful theorems some of which will themselves be machinery for later developments.

. . . .

THEOREM 2.3

If A and B are sets, then $A \cup B = B \cup A$.

PROOF

Let $x \in A \cup B$. Then $x \in A$ or $x \in B$ by Definition 2.8. Now $[(x \in A) \lor (x \in B)] \Leftrightarrow [(x \in B) \lor (x \in A)]$ by the commutative law for $\lor$. Hence, $x \in B$ or $x \in A$ and thus, $x \in B \cup A$ by Definition 2.8. Since x was an arbitrary element of $A \cup B$, we conclude that every element of $A \cup B$ is an element of $B \cup A$. Consequently, $A \cup B \subseteq B \cup A$ by Definition 2.1.

Let $y \in B \cup A$. Then $y \in B$ or $y \in A$ by Definition 2.8. But $[(y \in B) \lor (y \in A)] \Leftrightarrow [(y \in A) \lor (y \in B)]$ by the commutative law for $\lor$. Hence, $y \in A$ or $y \in B$ and thus, $y \in A \cup B$, by Definition 2.8. Since y was an arbitrary element of $B \cup A$, we conclude that every element of $B \cup A$ is an element of $A \cup B$. Consequently, $B \cup A \subseteq A \cup B$ by Definition 2.1.

Finally, since $A \cup B \subseteq B \cup A$ and $B \cup A \subseteq A \cup B$, we have $A \cup B = B \cup A$ by Theorem 2.2.   Q.E.D.

. . . .

THEOREM 2.4

If A and B are sets, then $A \cap B = B \cap A$.

The proof of this theorem is analogous to the proof of Theorem 2.3 and will be left to the reader as an exercise at the end of the section.

. . . .

THEOREM 2.5

If A, B, and C are sets, then

$$(A \cup B) \cup C = A \cup (B \cup C)$$

PROOF

Let $x \in (A \cup B) \cup C$. Then $x \in (A \cup B)$ or $x \in C$ by Definition 2.8. By applying Definition 2.8 again, we have $(x \in A \lor x \in B) \lor x \in C$. By the associative law for $\lor$ we have $x \in A \lor (x \in B \lor x \in C)$. Therefore, $x \in A$ or $x \in B \cup C$ by Definition 2.8. Again, by Definition 2.8, $x \in A \cup (B \cup C)$. Since x was an arbitrary element of $(A \cup B) \cup C$, it follows that every element of $(A \cup B) \cup C$ is an element of $A \cup (B \cup C)$ and hence $(A \cup B) \cup C \subseteq A \cup (B \cup C)$.

In a similar manner, letting y be an arbitrary element of $A \cup (B \cup C)$, we may show that $y \in (A \cup B) \cup C$ and hence that $A \cup (B \cup C) \subseteq (A \cup B) \cup C$.

Therefore, since $(A \cup B) \cup C \subseteq A \cup (B \cup C)$ and $A \cup (B \cup C) \subseteq$

$(A \cup B) \cup C$, we conclude that $(A \cup B) \cup C = A \cup (B \cup C)$ by Theorem 2.2.

Q.E.D.

. . . .

THEOREM 2.6

If A, B, and C are sets, then

$$(A \cap B) \cap C = A \cap (B \cap C)$$

We will leave the proof of this theorem to the reader as an exercise at the end of this section. The pattern of proof is the same as that of Theorem 2.5.

. . . .

If we think of sets as analogous to real numbers, set union as analogous to addition of real numbers, and set intersection as analogous to multiplication of numbers, then we notice that the theorems just proved are analogous to the commutative and associative laws of addition and multiplication of real numbers. These laws state that if a, b, and c are real numbers then

(i) $a + b = b + a$; $a \cdot b = b \cdot a$

(ii) $(a + b) + c = a + (b + c)$; $(a \cdot b) \cdot c = a \cdot (b \cdot c)$

In the real numbers, the distributive law asserts that if a, b, and c are real numbers, then

(iii) $a \cdot (b + c) = (a \cdot b) + (a \cdot c)$

In rules (i) and (ii), $+$ and $\cdot$ play identical roles, i.e., we could replace each occurrence of $+$ by $\cdot$ and each occurrence of $\cdot$ by $+$ and still have true statements. It is not true, however, that if a, b, and c are arbitrary real numbers, that

(iv) $a + (b \cdot c) = (a + b) \cdot (a + c)$

We will show that rule (iii) and the false statement (iv) are both true when we substitute arbitrary sets for the real numbers a, b, and c and substitute $\cup$ and $\cap$ for $+$ and $\cdot$, respectively. The proofs are given in the next two theorems.

. . . .

THEOREM 2.7

If A, B, and C are sets, then

$$A \cap (B \cup C) = (A \cap B) \cup (A \cap C)$$

PROOF

Let $x \in A \cap (B \cup C)$. Then $x \in A$ and $x \in (B \cup C)$ from Definition 2.10. By Definition 2.8 it follows that $x \in A$ and ($x \in B$ or $x \in C$), i.e., $(x \in A) \wedge [(x \in B) \vee (x \in C)]$, which is equivalent to $[(x \in A) \wedge (x \in B)] \vee [(x \in A) \wedge (x \in C)]$ by Exercise 1.5–14. Thus, by Definition 2.10, $(x \in A \cap B)$ or $(x \in A \cap C)$ from which we may conclude that $x \in (A \cap B) \cup (A \cap C)$ by Definition 2.8. Since x was an arbitrary element of $A \cap (B \cup C)$, we may infer that every element of $A \cap (B \cup C)$ is an element of $(A \cap B) \cup (A \cap C)$, or that $A \cap (B \cup C) \subseteq (A \cap B) \cup (A \cap C)$ by Definition 2.1.

Now let $y \in (A \cap B) \cup (A \cap C)$. By Definition 2.8 we infer that $y \in (A \cap B)$ or $y \in (A \cap C)$ and thus $(y \in A \wedge y \in B) \vee (y \in A \wedge y \in C)$ by Definition 2.10. Again using Exercise 1.5–14, this is equivalent to saying $(y \in A) \wedge (y \in B \vee y \in C)$. Therefore, $(y \in A)$ and $(y \in B \cup C)$ by Definition 2.8 or $y \in A \cap (B \cup C)$ from Definition 2.10. Since y was an arbitrary element of $(A \cap B) \cup (A \cap C)$, we conclude that every element of $(A \cap B) \cup (A \cap C)$ is an element of $A \cap (B \cup C)$. Consequently, $(A \cap B) \cup (A \cap C) \subseteq A \cap (B \cup C)$ by Definition 2.1.

Finally, having shown that $A \cap (B \cup C) \subseteq (A \cap B) \cup (A \cap C)$ and $(A \cap B) \cup (A \cap C) \subseteq A \cap (B \cup C)$, it follows that $A \cap (B \cup C) = (A \cap B) \cup (A \cap C)$ by Theorem 2.2.   Q.E.D.

. . . .

With the substitutions agreed upon in the paragraph preceding Theorem 2.7, it is seen that Theorem 2.7 is analogous to rule (iii), the distributive law of the real numbers. Statement (iv) also becomes a theorem when the substitutions are made, and yields another distributive law.

. . . .

THEOREM 2.8

If A, B, and C are sets, then

$$A \cup (B \cap C) = (A \cup B) \cap (A \cup C)$$

Because the proof of this theorem is similar to the proof of Theorem 2.7, we leave the proof to the reader as an exercise at the end of this section.

. . . .

Earlier in this chapter we gave an alternate proof to Theorem 2.1 by the indirect method. In order that the reader may have another example of this method of proof, we shall use the indirect method in proving the next theorem. Notice that the negation of the conclusion is used as an hypothesis.

. . . .

THEOREM 2.9

If A and B are sets, then $A \cap (B - A) = \emptyset$.

PROOF

Assume that $A \cap (B - A) \neq \emptyset$. Then there exists an x such that $x \in A \cap (B - A)$. By Definition 2.10, $x \in A$ and $x \in (B - A)$. Hence, from Definition 2.7, it follows that $(x \in A) \wedge (x \in B \wedge x \notin A)$. But, $x \in A$ and $x \notin A$ violates the law of contradiction. Therefore, by reductio ad absurdum, $A \cap (B - A) = \emptyset$ Q.E.D.

. . . .

The proof of the following theorem involves the use of the tautology known as "proof by cases" given as Exercise 1.5–4. In addition, the simple tautology given below will be used and the reader should verify that it is a tautology by means of a derived truth table:

$$(p \vee q) \Leftrightarrow [p \vee (q \wedge -p)]$$

It may help the reader to gain an intuitive grasp of the use of this tautology by sketching a Venn diagram of the union of sets A and B and the union of sets A and $B - A$.

. . . .

THEOREM 2.10

If A and B are sets, then $A \cup (B - A) = A \cup B$.

PROOF

Let $x \in A \cup (B - A)$. Then, by Definition 2.8, $x \in A$ or $x \in B - A$.

CASE 1: $x \in A$

$(x \in A) \Rightarrow (x \in A \vee x \in B)$ by Exercise 1.5–3 (laws of addition). Hence, $x \in A \cup B$.

CASE 2: $x \in B - A$

$(x \in B - A) \Rightarrow (x \in B \wedge x \notin A)$ by Definition 2.7. But $(x \in B \wedge x \notin A) \Rightarrow (x \in B)$, by Exercise 1.5–2 (laws of simplification), and hence $(x \in A \vee x \in B)$ by Exercise 1.5–3. Thus, $x \in A \cup B$.

Therefore, by the law of proof by cases, $(x \in A \vee x \in B - A) \Rightarrow x \in A \cup B$. Since x was chosen arbitrarily, every element of $A \cup (B - A)$ is an element of $A \cup B$ and it follows that $A \cup (B - A) \subseteq A \cup B$ by Definition 2.1.

Now let $y \in A \cup B$. Then $y \in A$ or $y \in B$ by Definition 2.8. Hence, by the tautology discussed just prior to the statement of the theorem, $(y \in A)$ or $(y \in B$ and $y \notin A)$. From Definition 2.7 we have $(y \in A)$ or $(y \in B - A)$ and, by Definition 2.8, $y \in A \cup (B - A)$. Since y was chosen arbitrarily, every element of $A \cup B$ is an element of $A \cup (B - A)$ and, by Definition 2.1, $A \cup B \subseteq A \cup (B - A)$.

Finally, since $A \cup (B - A) \subseteq A \cup B$ and $A \cup B \subseteq A \cup (B - A)$, we have $A \cup (B - A) = A \cup B$ by Theorem 2.2.   Q.E.D.

. . . .

THEOREM 2.11

If A, B, and C are sets, where $A \subseteq C$, $B \subseteq C$, $A \cup B = C$, and $A \cap B = \varnothing$, then $B = C - A$.

PROOF

Let $x \in C - A$. Then $x \in C$ and $x \notin A$ by Definition 2.7. Therefore, since $C = A \cup B$, $x \in A \cup B$ and $x \notin A$. Then, by Definition 2.8, $(x \in A \vee x \in B) \wedge (x \notin A)$ which, by Exercise 1.5–5, implies $x \in B$. Since x was an arbitrary element of $C - A$, every element of $C - A$ is an element of B. Therefore $C - A \subseteq B$ by Definition 2.1.

Let $y \in B$. Then $y \in C$ by Definition 2.1 since $B \subseteq C$. Now if $y \in A$, then $A \cap B \neq \varnothing$, which with the hypothesis $A \cap B = \varnothing$, violates the law of contradiction. Hence, $y \in C$ and $y \notin A$, so that $y \in C - A$ by Definition 2.7. Again, y was chosen arbitrarily and therefore every element of B is an element of $C - A$, and from Definition 2.1 we conclude $B \subseteq C - A$.

Therefore, by Theorem 2.2, with $C - A \subseteq B$ and $B \subseteq C - A$ it follows that $B = C - A$.   Q.E.D.

. . . .

We conclude this portion of our development of set theory with a theorem credited to De Morgan. We prove the first part for the reader and, since the pattern of the proof of the second part is similar to that of the first, we leave the proof of that part as an exercise to be proved at the end of the section.

. . . .

THEOREM 2.12

If A, B, and C are sets, then

(i) $C - (A \cup B) = (C - A) \cap (C - B)$
(ii) $C - (A \cap B) = (C - A) \cup (C - B)$

PROOF OF PART (i)

Let $x \in C - (A \cup B)$. Then $x \in C$ and $x \notin (A \cup B)$ by Definition 2.7. Now $x \notin (A \cup B)$ is the negation of the statement $x \in (A \cup B)$, i.e., the negation of $(x \in A \vee x \in B)$, by Definition 2.8. Therefore, by Exercise 1.5–11, we conclude $x \notin A$ and $x \notin B$. With $(x \in C) \wedge (x \notin A \wedge x \notin B)$, we may conclude $(x \in C \wedge x \notin A) \wedge (x \in C \wedge x \notin B)$. (The trivial tautology being used here is $[p \wedge (q \wedge r)] \Leftrightarrow [(p \wedge q) \wedge (p \wedge r)]$, which the reader may quickly verify.) Therefore, $x \in C - A$ and $x \in C - B$ by Definition 2.7.

Hence, by Definition 2.10, $x \in (C - A) \cap (C - B)$. Since x was chosen arbitrarily, every element of $C - (A \cup B)$ is an element of $(C - A) \cap (C - B)$ and by Definition 2.1, $C - (A \cup B) \subseteq (C - A) \cap (C - B)$.

Let $y \in (C - A) \cap (C - B)$. Then $y \in C - A$ and $y \in C - B$ by Definition 2.10. Hence, by Definition 2.7, $(y \in C \wedge y \notin A) \wedge (y \in C \wedge y \notin B)$. By the tautology mentioned in the preceding paragraph, this is the same as saying $(y \in C) \wedge (y \notin A \wedge y \notin B)$. Thus, we have $y \in C$ and $y \notin A \cup B$ by Exercise 1.5-11. Hence, $y \in C - (A \cup B)$ by Definition 2.7. Since y was an arbitrary element of $(C - A) \cap (C - B)$, we conclude that every element of $(C - A) \cap (C - B)$ is an element of $C - (A \cup B)$ and hence that $(C - A) \cap (C - B) \subseteq C - (A \cup B)$ by Definition 2.1.

Therefore, with the results of the two preceding paragraphs, we have $C - (A \cup B) = (C - A) \cap (C - B)$ by Theorem 2.2. Q.E.D.

PROOF OF PART (ii)

The proof of this part will be left as an exercise at the end of this section.

. . . .

EXERCISES

If A, B, C, and D are sets, prove the following.

1. Theorem 2.4.

2. Theorem 2.6.

3. Theorem 2.8.

4. Theorem 2.12, (ii).

5. $A \cup \varnothing = A$.

6. $A \cap \varnothing = \varnothing$.

7. $A \cup A = A$.

8. $A \cap A = A$.

9. If $A \subseteq B$, then
   (i) $B = A \cup B$.
   (ii) $A = A \cap B$.

10. $A \subseteq A \cup B$.

11. $A \cap B \subseteq A$.

12. If $B \subseteq C$, then $(A \cap B) \subseteq (A \cap C)$.

13. If $A \subseteq C$ and $B \subseteq C$, then $(A \cup B) \subseteq C$.

14. If $A \subseteq C$ and $B \subseteq D$, then $(A \cup B) \subseteq (C \cup D)$.

15. $A \subseteq \emptyset$ if and only if $A = \emptyset$.

16. If $A \subseteq C$ and $B \subseteq C$, then
    (i) $A \subseteq (C - B)$ if and only if $A \cap B = \emptyset$.
    (ii) $(C - B) \subseteq A$ if and only if $A \cup B = C$.

17. $(A - B) \cup (B - A) = (A \cup B) - (A \cap B)$.

18. $(A - C) \cup (B - C) = (A \cup B) - C$.

3

SETS AND FUNCTIONS

3.1 INTRODUCTION

The notion of function appears in many branches of mathematics including algebra, geometry, trigonometry, analysis, topology and statistics. As a student continues his study in these areas, he may find that each subject offers an apparently new and different definition of function. As a result, he may feel that each subject has its own special brand of function. Of course, the mature mathematician makes allowances for the differences in these definitions and uses his own generalization of the notion, but the beginning student is often confused by the apparent differences.

The purpose of this chapter is to develop a definition of function which will apply equally well to algebra, geometry, analysis, and other areas of mathematics to which set theory may be applied.

We will thereby add support to our claim that set theory plays a role of unifier and simplifier in mathematics.

3.2 ORDERED PAIRS

As a first step in the direction of the definition of function, we will define what is meant by the words "ordered pair." What we want is a definition of an object, which we will call an ordered pair, in terms of the set theory already developed. That is to say, we want a definition given in terms of "set" or "element of a set" in order that we may avoid the introduction of another undefined term.* Furthermore, we will not be satisfied with the definition unless it gives the object the important characteristic of an ordered pair which the reader has already encountered in analytic geometry; namely, the ordered pair (a,b) equals the ordered pair (c,d) if and only if $a = c$ and $b = d$.

Let a and b be elements of set C. Suppose we define the ordered pair (a,b) to be the set $\{a,b\}$. Such a definition is given in terms of the set theory already developed but we are not satisfied with this definition since $\{a,b\} = \{b,a\}$, whether or not $a = b$, by the Axiom of Extent.

Again, let a and b be elements of set C. In the following theorem we show that $\{\{a\}, \{a,b\}\}$ is a set which has the characteristic described above. Notice that this set consists of the two sets $\{a\}$ and $\{a,b\}$ which are equal if and only if $a = b$.

. . . .

THEOREM 3.1

Let a and b be elements of set C. Then $\{\{a\}, \{a,b\}\} = \{\{c\}, \{c,d\}\}$ if and only if $a = c$ and $b = d$.

---

* Actually, there is no harm in introducing another primitive (indeed, we shall find occasion to do so more than once in what follows). It happens that, in this case, it is easy to define the concept in terms of the theory already developed.

PROOF

If $a = c$ and $b = d$, then $\{a\} = \{c\}$ and $\{a,b\} = \{c,d\}$ by the Axiom of Extent. Applying that axiom again, we obtain $\{\{a\}, \{a,b\}\} = \{\{c\}, \{c,d\}\}$.

Suppose $\{\{a\}, \{a,b\}\} = \{\{c\}, \{c,d\}\}$. By the Axiom of Extent, $\{a\}$ and $\{a,b\}$ are both elements of the set $\{\{c\}, \{c,d\}\}$. Then $(\{a\} = \{c\}$ and $\{a,b\} = \{c,d\})$ or $(\{a\} = \{c,d\}$ and $\{a,b\} = \{c\})$. If $\{a\} = \{c\}$ and $\{a,b\} = \{c,d\}$ then $(a = c)$ and $[(a = c$ and $b = d)$ or $(a = d$ and $b = c)]$ by the Axiom of Extent. It then follows that $(a = c$ and $b = d)$ or $(a = c$ and $a = d$ and $b = c)$ by Exercise 1.5–14. This implies $(a = c$ and $b = d)$ or $(a = c$ and $b = c = a = d)$ so that $a = c$ and $b = d$. On the other hand, if $\{a\} = \{c,d\}$ and $\{a,b\} = \{c\}$, then $c \in \{a\}$, $d \in \{a\}$ and $a \in \{c\}$, $b \in \{c\}$ by the Axiom of Extent. Hence, $c = a$, $d = a$, and $a = c$, $b = c$. Thus, $a = c$ and $b = c = a = d$ so that $a = c$ and $b = d$. In both cases, $a = c$ and $b = d$.

Finally, $\{\{a\}, \{a,b\}\} = \{\{c\}, \{c,d\}\}$ if and only if $a = c$ and $b = d$ by Exercise 1.5–8.   Q.E.D.

. . . .

Since the set $\{\{a\}, \{a,b\}\}$ has the characteristic desired of an ordered pair, we make the following definition.

. . . .

DEFINITION 3.1

Let a and b be elements of set C. The set $\{\{a\}, \{a,b\}\}$ will be called the *ordered pair a, b*, denoted (a,b). Thus, $(a,b) = \{\{a\}, \{a,b\}\}$.

. . . .

Observe that $(a,b) = \{\{a\}, \{a,b\}\} = \{\{a\}, \{b,a\}\} = \{\{a,b\}, \{a\}\} = \{\{b,a\}, \{a\}\}$ by the Axiom of Extent so that we attach no significance to the order in which the names of the elements in the set $\{\{a\}, \{a,b\}\}$ are listed.

In analytic geometry we speak of the first coordinate a and the second coordinate b of the ordered pair (a,b). In order to be consistent with this usage, we will use these terms and give them in the following definition.

. . . .

DEFINITION 3.2

If (a,b) is an ordered pair, then we say that a occupies the *first co-ordinate* of the ordered pair and that b occupies the *second coordinate*.

. . . .

Consider the ordered pair (a,a). By Definition 3.1 we have $(a,a) = \{\{a\}, \{a,a\}\}$. But $\{a,a\} = \{a\}$ by the Axiom of Extent which reduces (a,a) to $\{\{a\}, \{a\}\}$ and finally to $\{\{a\}\}$, i.e., the set consisting of the set whose single element is a. Therefore, $(a,a) = \{\{a\}\}$.

. . . .

EXERCISES

1. Prove that the definition $(a,b) = \{\{b\}, \{a,b\}\}$ satisfies the property $(a,b) = (c,d)$ if and only if $a = c$ and $b = d$.

2. Prove $\{\{a\}, \{a,b\}\} = \{\{a\}\}$ if and only if $a = b$.

3. Form a definition of ordered triple, (a,b,c), which satisfies the property $(a,b,c) = (d,e,f)$ if and only if $a = d$, $b = e$, and $c = f$.

3.3 CARTESIAN PRODUCT SETS

We have seen that an ordered pair may be defined as a set which has certain properties. We may, of course, form sets of these sets. For example, the set of all husband-wife pairs is a set of ordered pairs. Likewise, the set of points in the Euclidean plane is a set of ordered pairs with each first coordinate as an abscissa and each second coordinate as an ordinate of the point. Sets of ordered pairs play an important part in the definition of function which we are seeking. We give a special name to certain sets of ordered pairs as follows.

. . . .

DEFINITION 3.3

If A and B are sets, the set of all ordered pairs whose first coordinate is an element of A and whose second coordinate is an element of B is called the *Cartesian product of A and B*, denoted $A \times B$. Symbolically, $A \times B = \{(a,b); a \in A$ and $b \in B\}$. We agree that if $A = \emptyset$ or $B = \emptyset$, then $A \times B = \emptyset$.

. . . .

Here are a few examples of the Cartesian product of simple sets.

. . . .

EXAMPLES

(1) $A = \{1,2,3\}$; $B = \{I,II\}$; $A \times B = \{(1,I),(1,II),(2,I),(2,II),(3,I),(3,II)\}$.
(2) $C = \{a,b\}$; $D = \{x,y\}$; $C \times D = \{(a,x), (a,y), (b,x), (b,y)\}$; $D \times C = \{(x,a), (x,b), (y,a), (y,b)\}$.
(3) $F = \{1,2\}$; $F \times F = \{(1,1), (1,2), (2,1), (2,2)\}$.
(4) $G = \{p,q,r\}$; $G \times G = \{(p,p), (p,q), (p,r), (q,p), (q,q), (q,r), (r,p), (r,q), (r,r)\}$.

. . . .

Example (2) shows that it is not generally true that if A and B are arbitrary sets then $A \times B = B \times A$. In this example it is clear that $C \times D$ does not equal $D \times C$ since $(a,x) \in C \times D$ but $(a,x) \notin D \times C$ if we assume that $a \neq x$. If we think of the Cartesian product of sets as an operation on sets, as we did in the case of set union and set intersection, then Example (2) shows that the operation is a *non-commutative* one.

The four examples above considered only simple sets whose elements could be listed in a short space. Suppose we consider the set of real numbers, E_1, and form the Cartesian product $E_1 \times E_1$. Then $E_1 \times E_1$ may be given in the set builder notation by using the Axiom of Specification as follows:

$$E_1 \times E_1 = \{(x,y); x \text{ and } y \text{ are real numbers}\}$$

The set $E_1 \times E_1$ is the set of ordered pairs which we call the Euclidean plane, or Euclidean 2-space. The symbol E_2 will be used for the set $E_1 \times E_1$ and is usually read "Euclidean 2-space." The real numbers are often called "Euclidean 1-space"; hence the symbol E_1 which we have used for this set.

. . . .

EXERCISES

1. Under what circumstances will it be true that $A \times B = B \times A$?
2. Describe the following sets geometrically (sketch a figure):
    a. $\{(x,y); x = 1, y \in E_1\}$.
    b. $\{(x,y); x \in E_1, y \in E_1, x < 0, y > 0\}$.
    c. $\{(x,y); x = 1, y = 1\}$.
    d. $\{(x,y); x \in E_1, y \in E_1, |x + y| = 1\}$.
    e. $\{(x,y); x \in E_1, y \in E_1, |x| + |y| = 5\}$.
    f. $\{(x,y); x \in E_1, y \in E_1, (|x| + |y| = 5) \text{ or } (|x| - |y| = 5)\}$.
3. Prove that if A, B, and C are sets and $A \subseteq B$, then $A \times C \subseteq B \times C$.
4. If A, B, and C are sets, prove $A \times (B \cup C) = (A \times B) \cup (A \times C)$.
5. If A, B, and C are sets, prove $A \times (B \cap C) = (A \times B) \cap (A \times C)$.
6. If the following are theorems, prove them; otherwise give a counterexample:
    a. If A, B, and C are sets, then $(A \times B) \times C = A \times (B \times C)$.
    b. If A, B, and C are sets, then $A \cup (B \times C) = (A \times B) \cup (A \times C)$.

3.4 RELATIONS

We begin this section with the following definition.

. . . .

DEFINITION 3.4

Let A and B be sets. A *relation from A to B* is a subset of $A \times B$. Symbolically, r is a relation from A to B if and only if $r \subseteq A \times B$.

. . . .

Notice that we use lower case letters to stand for relations although relations are sets (contrary to the usual procedure wherein we use upper case letters for sets).

Examples of relations occur frequently in everyday experiences. For instance, if P is a well-defined set of people, then, "x is a son of y," "x is a sister of y," and "x is a pupil of y" are examples of sentences which determine relations. That is to say, the set of all ordered pairs of people in which the first coordinate is a son of the second coordinate forms a subset of $P \times P$. Sometimes we ambiguously refer to this set as simply the relation "is a son of" when no confusion will arise; however, a relation is a set and is not a verbal phrase. The first coordinate in this relation must be a male person but the second coordinate is either a father or a mother. Hence, if Jeff is the son of John, then (Jeff, John) is an element of the relation described by the phrase, "is a son of." Clearly some ordered pairs in $P \times P$ are not in the relation "is a son of."

In general, if r is a relation and (x,y) is an element of the relation r, we sometimes write x (r) y (which is read, "x is r-related to y") instead of $(x,y) \in r$.

In mathematics some of the relations are used so often that they have been given special symbols, and in this case we usually use the form x (r) y instead of the form $(x,y) \in r$. For example, the relation described by the phrase "is greater than" is a subset of $E_1 \times E_1$, where E_1 is the set of real numbers, and the special symbol used for this relation is $>$. Although we could write $(3,2) \in >$, we usually write $3 > 2$.

The Axiom of Specification enables us to describe relations as sets in the set builder notation. The relation "is a son of" may be written as follows:

$$s = \{(a,b); a \in P, b \in P, a \text{ is a son of } b\}$$

The relation "is greater than" may be written, somewhat ambiguously:

$$> = \{(x,y); x \in E_1, y \in E_1, x > y\}$$

Another example is given in the set t below.

$$t = \{(x,y); x \in E_1, y \in E_1, x^2 + y^2 = 1\}$$

In these relations it will be noticed that some ordered pairs in the appropriate Cartesian product are in the relation and some are not. In set t, $(1,0) \in t$ but $(1,1) \notin t$.

Suppose that $A = \{x,y\}$ and $B = \{a,b,c\}$. Then $A \times B = \{(x,a), (x,b), (x,c), (y,a), (y,b), (y,c)\}$. What relations from A to B are possible from Definition 3.4? Since any subset of $A \times B$ is a relation, there are $2^6 = 64$ possible relations from A to B because there are 2^6 sets in the power set $p(A \times B)$. Thus, $\{(x,a)\}$ is a relation from A to B as are $\{(x,a), (x,b), (y,c)\}$, $\{(y,a), (y,c)\}$, $A \times B$, and $\varnothing$. Although $A \times B$ is a relation from A to B, more often we will consider those relations which are proper subsets of $A \times B$.

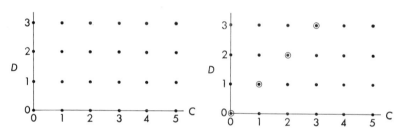

FIGURE 3.1 • The lattice points of $C \times D$

FIGURE 3.2 • Relation s from C to D

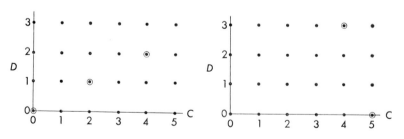

FIGURE 3.3 • Relation t from C to D

FIGURE 3.4 • Relation u from C to D

The structure of some relations can be illustrated by the following diagrammatical scheme. Let $C = \{0,1,2,3,4,5\}$ and $D = \{0,1,2,3\}$. Represent the elements of C along a horizontal axis and the elements of D along a vertical axis. The Cartesian product may then be represented by the twenty-four dots shown in Figure 3.1 where the usual coordinates of the dots correspond to the elements of $C \times D$. These dots are called *lattice points*. In Figure 3.2, circles have been placed around the lattice points of $C \times D$ which are in the relation $s = \{(x,y); x \in C, y \in D, x = y\}$. Similar diagrams can be drawn for the relations:

$$t = \{(x,y); x \in C, y \in D, x - 2y = 0\}$$
$$u = \{(x,y); x \in C, y \in D, x^2 + y^2 = 25\}$$

If r is a relation from A to B, we will often have occasion to refer to the set of all elements of A which are r-related to elements of B and to the set of all elements of B to which elements of A are r-related. We apply names and symbols to each of these sets of elements in the next definition.

. . . .

DEFINITION 3.5

Let r be a relation from A to B. The *domain of r*, denoted $\mathfrak{D}(r)$, is defined by $\mathfrak{D}(r) = \{x; x \in A \text{ and } (x,y) \in r \text{ for some } y \in B\}$. The *range of r*, denoted $\mathfrak{R}(r)$, is defined by $\mathfrak{R}(r) = \{y; y \in B \text{ and } (x,y) \in r$ for some $x \in A\}$.

. . . .

Clearly, $\mathfrak{D}(r) \subseteq A$ and $\mathfrak{R}(r) \subseteq B$. Moreover, the domain of r is simply the set of first coordinates in r and the range of r is simply the set of second coordinates in r.

There are some special relations which deserve consideration, and the remainder of this section will be devoted to an examination of some of these. If the reader will look again at Definition 3.4, he will see that nothing prohibits equality between A and B. In this case, however, it is a little awkward to speak of a relation from

A to A and the convention we adopt is to refer to such a relation as a relation *in* A. Many of the equations in elementary algebra determine relations *in* the set of real numbers E_1. For example, $r = \{(x,y); x \in E_1, y \in E_1, x^2 + 9y^2 = 9\}$ is a relation in E_1, i.e., a subset of $E_1 \times E_1$, which we call an ellipse. The domain of this relation, $\mathfrak{D}(r)$, is the set $\{x; x \in E_1, -3 \le x \le 3\}$ and the range, $\mathfrak{R}(r)$, is the set $\{y; y \in E_1, -1 \le y \le 1\}$.

Let $A = \{a,b,c\}$, $B = \{1,2,3\}$, and $r = \{(a,1), (a,3), (b,3), (c,3)\}$, so that r is a relation from A to B. The set $s = \{(1,a), (3,a), (3,b), (3,c)\}$, in which each ordered pair of r has been replaced by an ordered pair whose coordinates are the reverse of those in r, is clearly a subset of $B \times A$ and is therefore a relation from B to A. A relation formed in this way is said to be an *inverse* of the relation r. Thus, s is an inverse of the relation r. In Exercise 3.4–3 at the end of this section, the reader will be asked to prove that the inverse of a relation is unique so that we may speak of "*the* inverse of r," rather than the weaker phrase, "*an* inverse of r."

· ·

DEFINITION 3.6

Let r be a relation from A to B. The *inverse of* r, denoted r^{-1}, is a relation from B to A defined by $r^{-1} = \{(y,x); y \in B, x \in A, (x,y) \in r\}$.

· ·

Next, we consider the special relation in set A known as the *identity relation in* A.

· ·

DEFINITION 3.7

Let A be a set. The relation I_A, defined by $I_A = \{(x,y); x \in A, y \in A, x = y\}$, is called the *identity relation in* A.

· ·

I_A may be denoted I when it is clear which set A is involved. I_A may be defined even more simply as $\{(x,x); x \in A\}$. This relation has several interesting properties. First, for every element a of set A, $a = a$ so that $(a,a) \in I_A$. Second, if $a,b \in A$ and $a = b$, then $b = a$. Hence, if $(a,b) \in I_A$, then $(b,a) \in I_A$. Finally, if $a,b,c \in A$, $a = b$ and $b = c$, then $a = c$. Thus, if $(a,b) \in I_A$ and $(b,c) \in I_A$, then $(a,c) \in I_A$. These three properties of the identity relation are common to other relations and we classify such relations by means of our next definition.

. . . .

DEFINITION 3.8

Let r be a relation in A. r is an *equivalence relation in A* if and only if the following conditions hold in r:

(i) For each $a \in A$, $(a,a) \in r$. (*r* is *reflexive*)

(ii) If $(a,b) \in r$, then $(b,a) \in r$. (*r* is *symmetric*)

(iii) If $(a,b) \in r$ and $(b,c) \in r$, then $(a,c) \in r$. (*r* is *transitive*)

. . . .

Since the identity relation meets the conditions of Definition 3.8, it is an equivalence relation.

Let us consider next a few examples of relations in the set $A = \{1,2,3,4\}$. Some of these relations will meet all three conditions of Definition 3.8 and therefore qualify as equivalence relations while other relations may satisfy one or two of the conditions but not all three.

. . . .

EXAMPLES

(1) $r_1 = \{(1,1), (2,2), (3,3), (4,4), (1,2)\}$. Notice that for each element a of set A, $(a,a) \in r_1$ so that r_1 is a reflexive relation. However, since $(1,2) \in r_1$ and $(2,1) \notin r_1$, r_1 is not a symmetric relation and hence not an equivalence relation. Finally, r_1 satisfies condition (iii) in a trivial way and we conclude that r_1 is a transitive relation.

(2) $r_2 = \{(1,1), (2,2), (4,4), (1,2)\}$. Since $3 \in A$ and $(3,3) \notin r_2$, r_2 is

not a reflexive relation. Neither is r_2 a symmetric relation since $(2,1) \notin r_2$ but r_2 satisfies condition (iii) and is a transitive relation in A.

(3) $r_3 = \{(2,3), (3,2)\}$ is certainly not reflexive in A but it is symmetric. Since $(2,3) \in r_3$ and $(3,2) \in r_3$ we must have $(2,2) \in r_3$ if r_3 is to be transitive, but we see that such is not the case, so that r_3 is only symmetric in A.

(4) $r_4 = \{(1,3), (3,2), (1,2)\}$ is not reflexive nor is it symmetric but it plainly meets the condition for transitivity. Hence, r_4 is a transitive relation.

(5) $r_5 = \{(1,1), (2,2), (3,3), (4,4), (1,2), (2,1), (2,3), (3,2), (1,3), (3,1)\}$. By checking each element of A we see that r_5 is reflexive, and by checking each ordered pair in r_5 for the presence of its symmetric opposite we see that it is symmetric. Finally, r_5 is transitive since it satisfies condition (iii). Since r_5 is reflexive, symmetric, and transitive, r_5 is an equivalence relation.

(6) $r_6 = A \times A$. We list this example to point out that $A \times A$ is always an equivalence relation as can be easily verified by checking the three properties.

. . . .

One might be tempted to say that the requirement of reflexivity in equivalence relations is redundant, that is, if a relation is symmetric and transitive, it should follow that the relation is also reflexive because of the following line of argument:

Since the relation, r, is symmetric, then if $(a,b) \in r$ it follows that $(b,a) \in r$. Since r is transitive, it follows that with $(a,b) \in r$ and $(b,a) \in r$, $(a,a) \in r$. Hence, r is apparently reflexive.

The fallacy in the argument lies in the fact that the criterion for reflexivity is that $(a,a) \in r$ *for each* $a \in A$. The argument above would fail in each case where for some $a \in A$ there is no $b \in A$ such that $(a,b) \in r$. The example below illustrates a symmetric and transitive relation which is not reflexive (r_7 is a relation in set A of the examples above).

(7) $r_7 = \{(2,3), (3,2), (2,2), (3,3)\}$.

EXERCISES

1. Construct three or four relations and describe the domain and range of each.

2. Verify that the relation given by $r = \{(x,y);\ x \in E_1,\ y \in E_1,\ x^2 + y^2 + 2x = 4y - 6\}$ is empty. What is the domain and what is the range of r? Find suitable sets A and B as replacements for E_1 which will make r a non-empty relation from A to B.

3. If r is a relation from A to B and s and t are inverses of r from B to A, prove that $s = t$, thus proving that the inverse of r is unique.

4. If r is a relation from A to B, prove that

   (i) $\mathcal{D}(r^{-1}) = \mathcal{R}(r)$

   (ii) $\mathcal{R}(r^{-1}) = \mathcal{D}(r)$

   (Hint: Statements (i) and (ii) concern equality of sets, hence Theorem 2.2 should provide help.)

5. Sketch lattice point graphs of each of the relations r_1 to r_7 discussed in this section.

6. Given set $B = \{0,1,2,3,4\}$, form relations in B which satisfy the following requirements and sketch a lattice point graph of each of the eight relations.

	Reflexive	Symmetric	Transitive
(1)	yes	no	no
(2)	no	yes	no
(3)	no	no	yes
(4)	yes	yes	no
(5)	yes	no	yes
(6)	no	yes	yes
(7)	yes	yes	yes
(8)	no	no	no

7. As a result of the lattice point sketches drawn in the preceding exercises, what is a geometric characteristic of reflexive relations? symmetric relations? transitive relations?

8. What condition may we impose on a relation r in A in order to insure that reflexivity is a consequence of symmetry and transitivity?

9. If r is a relation from A to B, prove that $(r^{-1})^{-1} = r$. (Hint: remember we are still talking about sets.)

10. Prove the following theorems given that r is a relation in set A.

(i) If r is reflexive, then r^{-1} is reflexive.

(ii) If r is symmetric, then r^{-1} is symmetric.

(iii) If r is transitive, then r^{-1} is transitive.

From the above theorems draw the obvious conclusion.

11. Prove that the identity relation in A, I_A, is unique.

12. Prove that I_A is an equivalence relation in A.

13. Prove that $I_A^{-1} = I_A$.

3.5 PARTITIONS

With the completion of Section 3.4 we are but a step away from the major objective of this chapter, namely, the definition of function. It seems more appropriate at this point, however, to fully exploit the concepts just discovered, after which we will return to the main objective.

Let us consider a classroom full of students. Suppose that we wish to make some classification of the students in the room and choose to classify them by their grade in school. First, we examine the class roll to see what grades are represented by the students in the class. Suppose we find that there are only sophomores, juniors, and seniors present and decide to use these as our categories in the classification. Now notice that such a classification has the following three properties: first, every category will have at least one student in it; second, every student will fall into precisely one of the categories; and third, the union of the categories will be the set of students in the room. Classifications characterized by these three properties are important enough in mathematics to give them a special name.

. . . .

DEFINITION 3.9

Let A be a non-empty set. A *partition of A*, denoted $\mathcal{P}$, is a subset of the power set of A, $p(A)$, such that:

(i) If $C \in \mathcal{P}$, then $C \neq \emptyset$.

(ii) If $C_1 \in \mathcal{P}$, $C_2 \in \mathcal{P}$, and $C_1 \neq C_2$, then $C_1 \cap C_2 = \emptyset$.

(iii) $\displaystyle\bigcup_{C \in \mathcal{P}} C = A$.

. . . .

For example, we often classify the set of integers, Z, by means of the categories even and odd. If E represents the set of even integers and D represents the set of odd integers, then a partition, $\mathcal{P}$, of Z is the set $\{E, D\}$. Notice that $E \neq \emptyset$, $D \neq \emptyset$ satisfying property (i). Furthermore, no even integer is odd and no odd integer is even so that $E \cap D = \emptyset$. Finally, the union of E and D is the set Z and we have established that $\mathcal{P}$ is a partition of Z.

If $A = \{a_1, a_2, \ldots, a_n\}$, two simple partitions of A are

$$\{\{a_1\}, \{a_2\}, \ldots, \{a_n\}\}$$

and

$$\{\{a_1, a_2, \ldots, a_n\}\}$$

Clearly the conditions of Definition 3.9 are satisfied by both sets.

Consider another partition of the set of integers. Let $\mathcal{P}' = \{Z_0, Z_1, Z_2\}$, where

$$Z_0 = \{x;\, x \in Z,\, x = 3n \text{ for some } n \in Z\}$$
$$Z_1 = \{x;\, x \in Z,\, x = 3n + 1 \text{ for some } n \in Z\}$$
$$Z_2 = \{x;\, x \in Z,\, x = 3n + 2 \text{ for some } n \in Z\}$$

The set $\mathcal{P}'$ is a partition since Z_0, Z_1, and Z_2 are all non-empty, disjoint, and their union is the set Z of integers. We will return to this example from another point of view after a brief consideration of the following definition.

. . . .

DEFINITION 3.10

Let A be a non-empty set and r an equivalence relation in A. Furthermore, let a be an arbitrary element of A. The *equivalence class of a with respect to r*, denoted A_a, is defined by $A_a = \{x; x \in A$ and $(a,x) \in r\}$.

. . . .

For convenience, we will say that each element of A_a is "equivalent" to a as a short expression for the idea that a is r-related to every element of A_a and that r is an equivalence relation.

As an example, let Z be the set of integers and r the relation defined as follows:

$$r = \{(x,y); x \in Z, y \in Z, x - y = 3n \text{ for some } n \in Z\}$$

The reader will be asked to prove that r is an equivalence relation in Exercise 3.5–1. Now let us take one specific element from Z, say 7, and find the equivalence class of 7 with respect to r. What we want is the set of all integers to which 7 is r-related, i.e., the set of all integers y such that $7 - y$ is a multiple of 3. Thus, 4 is an integer to which 7 is r-related, as are the following: $1, -2, -5, -8, 7, 10$, etc. Hence it appears that the equivalence class of 7 with respect to r, Z_7, is the set $\{\ldots, -8,-5,-2,1,4,7,10, \ldots\}$. But this is the set $\{x; x \in Z, x = 3n + 1 \text{ for some } n \in Z\}$ which we called Z_1 in the example of partition $\wp'$ given just prior to Definition 3.10. Let us pick another specific integer, say 11, and find Z_{11}. Clearly $Z_{11} = \{\ldots, -7,-4,-1,2,5,8, \ldots\} = \{y; y \in Z, y = 3n + 2 \text{ for some } n \in Z\} = Z_2$ of the partition $\wp'$. Similarly $Z_{15} = Z_0$ of $\wp'$ and continued choices of arbitrary elements of Z show that Z_7, Z_{11}, and Z_{15} are the only distinct equivalence classes which we may form from the set Z and the equivalence relation r. Of course, we have seen that each equivalence class is identical to several others, for instance $Z_7 = Z_4 = Z_1 = Z_{-2} = Z_{142}$, but there are only three distinct classes. Furthermore, we have seen that each of these classes is the same as some element in the partition $\mathcal{P}'$. This fact suggests an important theorem which we shall prove shortly. First, however, we prove a lemma which shows the relationship between pairs of subscripts in identical equivalence classes like Z_7 and Z_{142}. The lemma will be quite helpful in the proof of the theorem.

. . . .

LEMMA 3.1

Let A be a non-empty set and r an equivalence relation in A. Furthermore, let a and b be arbitrary elements in A. Then $A_a = A_b$ if and only if $(a,b) \in r$.

PROOF

Suppose that $A_a = A_b$. Since r is an equivalence relation, r is reflexive, hence $(b,b) \in r$. Thus $b \in A_b$ by Definition 3.10. But $A_a = A_b$ so by the Axiom of Extent, $b \in A_a$. Therefore, $(a,b) \in r$ by Definition 3.10.

Suppose that $(a,b) \in r$. Let $x \in A_a$. Then $(a,x) \in r$ by Definition 3.10. But $(b,a) \in r$ since r is symmetric and $(b,a) \in r$ and $(a,x) \in r$ implies $(b,x) \in r$ since r is transitive. Therefore, $x \in A_b$, and since x was an arbitrary element of A_a, every element of A_a is an element of A_b. Thus, $A_a \subseteq A_b$.

Similarly, it may be shown that $A_b \subseteq A_a$ and we conclude that $A_a = A_b$ by Theorem 2.2.

Since $(A_a = A_b) \Rightarrow (a,b) \in r$, and $(a,b) \in r \Rightarrow (A_a = A_b)$, we may conclude that $(A_a = A_b) \Leftrightarrow (a,b) \in r$ by Exercise 1.5–8.   Q.E.D.

. . . .

THEOREM 3.2

An equivalence relation in a non-empty set A determines a partition of A and conversely.

PROOF

Let r be an equivalence relation in A and let $\mathcal{Q}$ be the set of all equivalence classes of A with respect to r, i.e., $\mathcal{Q} = \{A_a; a \in A\}$. Since

r is an equivalence relation, $(a,a) \in r \; \forall \; a \in A$. Thus if A_a is an equivalence class in $\mathcal{Q}$, $a \in A_a$ by Definition 3.10, and hence $A_a \neq \varnothing$. Also, every element a of A is an element of the equivalence class A_a in $\mathcal{Q}$ and we conclude that $\bigcup_{a \in A} A_a = A$ by Definition 2.9. Furthermore, if A_a and A_b are elements of $\mathcal{Q}$ and $A_a \cap A_b \neq \varnothing$, then $\exists \; x \in A_a \cap A_b$ or $x \in A_a$ and $x \in A_b$ by Definition 2.10. Thus, $(a,x) \in r$ and $(b,x) \in r$ by Definition 3.10. But r is symmetric so $(x,b) \in r$ and it follows that $(a,b) \in r$ since r is transitive. Then $A_a = A_b$ by Lemma 3.1. Thus, if $A_a \neq A_b$, then $A_a \cap A_b = \varnothing$. Therefore, $\mathcal{Q}$ is a partition of A by Definition 3.9 and is called *the partition of A induced by r* which is denoted $\mathcal{P}(r)$.

If $\mathcal{P}$ is any partition of A, define a relation s in A as follows: $s = \{(x,y); x \in A, y \in A, \text{ and } \exists \; C \in \mathcal{P} \text{ such that } x \in C \text{ and } y \in C\}$. Since $\bigcup_{C \in \mathcal{P}} C = A$ by Definition 3.9, for each $a \in A$, $\exists \; C \in \mathcal{P}$ such that $a \in C$. Hence $a \in C$, and $a \in C$ means $(a,a) \in s$ for each $a \in A$, by definition of s, and we conclude that s is reflexive. Now if $(a,b) \in s$, then $\exists \; C \in \mathcal{P}$ such that $a \in C$ and $b \in C$. But then $b \in C$ and $a \in C$ by Exercise 1.5–12, so that $(b,a) \in s$ by definition of s; therefore s is symmetric. Finally, if $(a,b) \in s$ and $(b,c) \in s$, then $\exists \; C_1 \in \mathcal{P}$ and $C_2 \in \mathcal{P}$ such that $a \in C_1$, $b \in C_1$, $b \in C_2$, and $c \in C_2$. Now $b \in C_1$ and $b \in C_2$ implies that $C_1 \cap C_2 \neq \varnothing$. Therefore, $C_1 = C_2$ by Definition 3.9, (ii). By substitution, $a \in C_1$ and $c \in C_2 = C_1$ so that $(a,c) \in s$ and we have shown s to be transitive. Therefore, s is an equivalence relation in A determined by the partition $\mathcal{P}$ and is called *the equivalence relation induced by $\mathcal{P}$* which is denoted $r(\mathcal{P})$.　　　　　　Q.E.D.

. . . .

As an example of the use of this theorem let us begin with a set $A = \{w,x,y,z\}$ and consider a partition of A as follows: $\mathcal{P} = \{\{w,x\}, \{y\}, \{z\}\}$. The theorem gives us the method for constructing the equivalence relation $r(\mathcal{P})$. Thus, (w,w) must be an element of $r(\mathcal{P})$ as well as (w,x), (x,w), (x,x), (y,y), (z,z). Hence the equivalence relation is:

$$r(\mathcal{P}) = \{(x,x), (w,w), (w,x), (x,w), (y,y), (z,z)\}$$

From $r(\mathcal{P})$ we obtain the equivalence classes:

$$A_w = \{w,x\} = A_x$$
$$A_y = \{y\}$$
$$A_z = \{z\}$$

so that $\mathcal{P}(r(\mathcal{P})) = \{A_w, A_y, A_z\} = \mathcal{P}$.

As a second example, let us begin with an equivalence relation in set $B = \{1,2,3,4,5\}$ defined as follows: $r = \{(1,1), (2,2), (3,3), (4,4), (5,5), (1,3), (3,1), (2,5), (5,2)\}$. Again the theorem yields a technique for the construction of the partition $\mathcal{P}(r)$. We first list the equivalence classes:

$$B_1 = \{1,3\} = B_3$$
$$B_2 = \{2,5\} = B_5$$
$$B_4 = \{4\}$$

Then the partition is given by $\mathcal{P}(r) = \{\{1,3\}, \{2,5\}, \{4\}\}$ and $r(\mathcal{P}(r)) = \{(1,1), (2,2), (3,3), (4,4), (5,5), (1,3), (3,1), (2,5), (5,2)\} = r$.

These two examples illustrate the interdependence of the induced relations and partitions upon the given relations and partitions.

. . . .

EXERCISES

1. Prove that the relation $r = \{(x,y); x \in Z, y \in Z, x - y = 3n$ for some $n \in Z\}$ is an equivalence relation.

2. Given $C = \{u,v,w,x,y,z\}$, exhibit an equivalence relation in C and show the partition induced by it. Also exhibit a partition of C and show the equivalence relation induced by the partition.

3. Draw a lattice point graph of the equivalence relation r given in the second example above. What are some geometric characteristics of the partition $\mathcal{P}(r)$?

3.6 FUNCTIONS

We now return to the main theme of this chapter and give the definition of function below.

· ·

DEFINITION 3.11

Let A and B be sets. A *function*, denoted f, *from* A *to* B is a relation from A to B such that:

(i) $\mathfrak{D}(f) = A$

(ii) If $(x,y) \in f$ and $(x,z) \in f$, then $y = z$. We write, $f \colon A \longrightarrow B$, which is read, "$f$ is a function from A to B."

· ·

This definition shows that a function from A to B is simply a special relation from A to B having the property that its domain is A and the property that no two different ordered pairs in the relation have the same first coordinate.

As we stated in the introduction to this chapter, the definition of function given here is intended to apply to all branches of mathematics to which set theory is applicable. Therefore, we should explain why this particular definition is a desirable one, and we should compare it with what the reader may have seen or heard elsewhere concerning the word "function."

First of all, let us examine property (i) of the definition. The requirement that $\mathfrak{D}(f) = A$ is an arbitrary choice since we could define a function properly without such a requirement. However, since we will speak of a function *from* A to B, it seems appropriate to make requirement (i). In addition, in the work which is to follow, the use of requirement (i) will make the statement of definitions and theorems involving functions easier than would otherwise be the case. The reader may wonder why we did not require $\mathfrak{R}(f) = B$. Again, this was an arbitrary choice since a proper definition of function could be made using this as a requirement. But, in the work of this text, we believe that omitting the requirement $\Re(f) = B$ will make for a better development. Thus, when we write $f: A \longrightarrow B$, we will insist that $\mathfrak{D}(f) = A$ but $\Re(f)$ may be a proper subset of B.

Now let us consider requirement (ii). Why is it necessary to have one and only one second coordinate for each first coordinate in the function? Admittedly, for many years the word "function" was used in connection with relations which did not satisfy this requirement. These were the so-called multiple-valued functions which still play an important role in mathematics. However, in the bulk of the circumstances to be considered in this text, we will want to use those relations restricted by (ii) and so we isolate such relations and call them functions.

Before we turn to the comparison of our definition of function with some of those which the reader may have found elsewhere, several remarks are in order concerning the terminology associated with functions. Since mathematics is a discipline which is constantly growing and changing, it is only natural that terms invented many years ago will now be used in ways different from their original meaning. For example, suppose $f: A \longrightarrow B$ is a function. Whenever $(x,y) \in f$ we sometimes write $y = f(x)$ and say that y is the *value* of the function f at x. The use of $y = f(x)$ as an abbreviation for $(x,y) \in f$ is traditional and we shall probably be using it for many years to come, but we are using it as an abbreviation although it was originally used to express the idea that f was "acting" upon x and producing y. Notice also that it is not consistent with Definition 3.11 to speak of "the function $f(x)$" or "the function $y = f(x)$" since the name of the function is "f." However, these phrases are still used, especially in analysis, and it is probable that we shall continue to use them but it should be recognized that they are merely traditional ways of speaking of the function f.

One of the common definitions of function is given in terms of variables as follows. A variable y *is a function of* a variable x if y *depends* on x in such a way that for each *value assumed* by x we can

obtain *at least* one *value* for y. The word "depends" is usually not
defined but is left to the intuition of the reader. Notice that the
connotation of action is present in this definition; that is, it would
seem as if x is moving around and assuming various values and "we"
obtain a value for y. From Definition 3.11 it is clear that a function
involves no action since it is simply a set. The definition above
also allows more than one second coordinate for each first coordinate
thereby giving rise to the notion of multiple-valued functions.

Two terms arise from the definition given in the preceding paragraph which are often found in the literature; namely, *independent*
variable and *dependent* variable. The variable x in the definition
above is called the independent variable and the variable y is called
the dependent variable. In our definition of function we did not
need to introduce these two terms, but it is clear that the independent variable refers to an arbitrary member of the domain of
the function and the dependent variable refers to the corresponding
member of the range of the function.

Another definition of function is often stated as follows. A
function is a *rule* which associates with each value of one variable x
one or more values of another variable y. These "rules" are usually
stated in equation form and do not appear to be sets of ordered pairs.
The word "associates" is usually left to the intuition of the reader
after a few convincing examples are given. The terms independent
and dependent are also derived from this definition.

To illustrate the use of Definition 3.11 and the definitions
given above, consider what is meant by "the function $y = x^2$."
To be precise we really mean the function f, defined by

$$f = \{(x,y); x \in E_1, y \in E_1 \text{ and } y = x^2\}$$

In the latter form we emphasize the essentials of the function;
namely, it is a set of ordered pairs, a subset of $E_1 \times E_1$, and in every
ordered pair the second coordinate is the square of the first coordinate. Certainly, the statement "$y = x^2$" is not the function, because
the function is the set of ordered pairs described by f. Yet, we might

speak of "the function $y = x^2$" if we keep in mind that we really mean the function f. If we are given the statement "$y = x^2$" and from the context realize that it is to determine a function in E_1, then we may reconstruct a function f precisely as given above.

Several terms are often used synonymously with the word function. Among them is the word "mapping" which comes from a branch of mathematics called topology and another is the word "correspondence." A function is sometimes called a correspondence because to each element x of a set A there is said to *correspond* a unique, or single, element y in a set B. Henceforth, we will use the words function, mapping, and correspondence interchangeably, but whichever word we use the meaning is given in Definition 3.11.

Through topology, another term has been found useful in set theory and is given in the next definition.

. . . .

DEFINITION 3.12

If A and B are sets, $f\colon A \longrightarrow B$, and $(x,y) \in f$, then we say that y is the *image* of x and write $y = f(x)$.

. . . .

Observe that the definition refers to *the* image of x since each $x \in A$ has only one image by Definition 3.11. Using the term defined here, Definition 3.11, (ii) could be stated, "Each element of A has a unique image." It is obvious that the set of all images of the elements of set A is the range of f. Hence, we often speak of the range of a function as the *image of its domain*. More generally, if $f\colon A \longrightarrow B$ and $A' \subseteq A$, then the set $B' = \{y; y \in B, y = f(x)$ for some $x \in A'\}$ is called the *image of A' under f* and we write $f(A') = B'$. Now the symbol $f(A')$ is ambiguous since it has been previously used to denote that unique member of B which is the image of an element in $\mathfrak{D}(f)$ and ordinarily $A' \not\subseteq A$ and $B' \not\subseteq B$. Even so, the notation is sometimes very convenient and is commonly employed so that we bow to convention and adopt it with the warning that it should never be used when any confusion might arise. For instance, if the elements of A are themselves sets (usually, but not always, we would then use a script letter instead of A) the symbol $f(A')$ by itself might have two meanings.

. . . .

EXAMPLES

(1) $A = \{a,b,c,d\}$, $B = \{x,y,z\}$, $f = \{(a,x), (b,x), (c,x), (d,y)\}$. $\mathcal{R}(f) = \{x,y\}$. Notice that $\mathcal{R}(f) \subset B$.

(2) $C = \{1,2,3,4,5\}$, $D = \{\text{I,II}\}$, $g = \{(1,\text{I}), (2,\text{II}), (3,\text{I}), (4,\text{II}), (5,\text{II})\}$. $\mathcal{R}(f) = \{\text{I,II}\}$. Here, $\mathcal{R}(g) = D$.

(3) $A = E_1 = B$. $h = \{(x,y); x, y \in E_1, x - y = 3\}$. $\mathcal{R}(h) = E_1$.

(4) $A = Z = B$. $j = \{(x,y); x,y \in Z, y = x^2\}$. $\mathcal{R}(j) = \{0,1,4,9,16, \ldots\} \subset B$.

(5) $A = \{m,n,p,q\}$, $B = \{s,t,u,v,w\}$, $k = \{(m,s), (n,t), (p,u), (q,v)\}$. $\mathcal{R}(f) = \{s,t,u,v\} \subset B$.

. . . .

EXERCISES

1. Decide whether or not the following are functions from A to B where $A = \{1,2,3,4,5\}$ and $B = \{a,b,c,d,e\}$. If they are functions, give the range of each. If they are not, tell why.

   a. $f = \{(1,a), (2,b), (3,b), (5,e)\}$.
   b. $g = \{(2,a), (3,a), (1,a), (5,a), (4,a)\}$.
   c. $h = \{(1,e), (5,d), (3,a), (2,b), (1,d), (4,a)\}$.
   d. $j = \{(1,a), (2,b), (3,c), (4,x), (4,e)\}$.
   e. $k = \{(5,a), (1,e), (4,b), (3,c), (2,d)\}$.

2. The following may or may not be functions from E_1 to E_1. If they are functions, give the range of each and if they are not, tell why.

   a. $s = \{(x,y); x, y \in E_1, y = \sqrt{x}\}$.
   b. $t = \{(x,y); x, y \in E_1, x^2 + y^2 = 1\}$.
   c. $u = \{(x,y); x, y \in E_1, x - y = 2\}$.
   d. $v = \{(x,y); x, y \in E_1, y = 1\}$.
   e. $w = \{(x,y); x, y \in E_1, y = 2$ when $x < 0$, $y = -2$ when $x > 0$, and $y = 0$ when $x = 0\}$.

3. Prove that the identity relation I_A is a function, hereafter called the *identity function*.

3.7 TYPES OF FUNCTIONS

On close examination of the examples of functions given in the preceding section, the reader may have noticed that there are different types of functions. The following definition will serve to classify the types of functions to be considered in this text.

· ·

DEFINITION 3.13

Let A and B be sets and $f: A \longrightarrow B$.

(i) f is *one-to-one* (abbreviated 1–1) if whenever $(x_1,y) \in f$ and $(x_2,y) \in f$ then $x_1 = x_2$. We write, $f: A \xrightarrow[1\text{-}1]{} B$.

(ii) If f is not 1–1, f is called *many-to-one*.

(iii) f is said to be a function from A *onto* B if $\Re(f) = B$. We write, $f: A \xrightarrow{\text{onto}} B$.

(iv) If f is not onto B, then f is said to be *into* B.

(v) If f is 1–1 and onto B, then f is said to be a 1–1 *correspondence* between A and B. We write, $f: A \xrightarrow[1\text{-}1]{\text{onto}} B$.

· ·

Take care to notice the difference between Definition 3.13, (i) and Definition 3.11, (ii). A function must have the property that each element of A has a unique image. However, several elements of A may have the same image and such functions are many-to-one. When it happens that each element of $\Re(f)$ is the image of a unique element of A then the function is 1–1. Thus, if we are given a function f and must prove that it is 1–1, we may do so by showing that if $f(x_1) = f(x_2)$ then $x_1 = x_2$, where x_1 and x_2 are arbitrary elements of the domain of f.   Another proof may be given by using the law of the contrapositive, i.e., showing that if $x_1 \neq x_2$ then $f(x_1) \neq f(x_2)$.

In Figure 3.5, sets A and B are the sets of isolated dots within the circles.   All of the elements of A are paired with some element

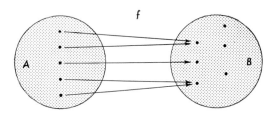

FIGURE 3.5 • A many-to-one function from A into B

of B by means of the lines drawn between them.   This set of pairs of elements is a function f from A into B and, since some of the elements of $\mathcal{R}(f)$ are images of more than one element of A, f is not a 1–1 function.

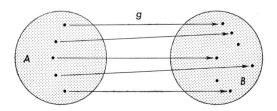

FIGURE 3.6 • A 1–1 function from A into B

In Figure 3.6, sets A and B are represented in a fashion similar to Figure 3.5.   The set of pairs of points represents the function g, which is a 1–1 function from A into B since each element in $\mathcal{R}(g)$ is paired with one and only one element of A.

In connection with part (iii) of Definition 3.13, we already are familiar with the fact that $\Re(f) \subseteq B$ since f is a function from A to B. If we are asked to verify that a given function, say f, is onto B, we may show that $B \subseteq \Re(f)$ and by Theorem 2.2 we have $\Re(f) = B$. Thus, to prove that a function is "onto," we show that

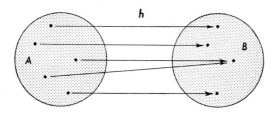

FIGURE 3.7 • A function from A onto B

if $y \in B$, $\exists\, x \in A$ such that $(x,y) \in f$, so that $y \in \Re(f)$. Having chosen y arbitrarily, every element of B is an element of $\Re(f)$, hence $B \subseteq \Re(f)$. Therefore, $\Re(f) = B$ by Theorem 2.2 and f is onto B, or we say simply "onto." Figure 3.7 illustrates a function h from A onto B. Notice that h is not 1–1.

Figure 3.8 illustrates a function from A to B which is 1–1 and

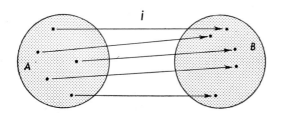

FIGURE 3.8 • A 1–1 correspondence between A and B

onto, that is, a function which is a 1–1 correspondence between A and B. Observe that every element of B is the image of a single element of A. In Figure 3.8 it is intuitively obvious that sets A and B have the same number of elements. In Chapter 5 we will make

use of the special function called 1–1 correspondence in our definition of number.

. . . .

EXAMPLES

(1) Let $f = \{(x,y); x \in E_1, y \in E_1, y = 2x + 3\}$. By its definition, f is
a relation in E_1 and for each x in E_1 ∃ $y = 2x + 3$ in E_1, hence
$\mathfrak{D}(f) = E_1$. Furthermore, if $(x,y) \in f$ and $(x,z) \in f$ then $y = 2x + 3$
and $z = 2x + 3$, therefore $y = z$ and, by showing that the relation f
satisfies Definition 3.11, we have shown that f is a function. Is f an
onto function? For each $y \in E_1$ there exists $x = (y - 3)/2$ such that
$y = 2x + 3$ and since $(y - 3)/2 \in E_1$ we conclude that f is onto by
the argument preceding Figure 3.7. Is f a 1–1 function? We easily
show that it is for we know that if $(x_1,y), (x_2,z) \in f$ then $x_1 = (y - 3)/2$
and $x_2 = (y - 3)/2$. Thus $x_1 = x_2$ and f is 1–1. Therefore, f is a
1–1 function from E_1 onto E_1, i.e., a 1–1 correspondence.

(2) Let $f = \{(x,y); x \in E_1, y \in E_1, y = \sqrt{x}\}$. Since $y \in E_1$, x cannot be
replaced by any negative element of E_1 for if x is a negative real number, then y is not real but complex. Therefore, no ordered pairs in
this relation have negative first coordinates and, since $\mathfrak{D}(f) \neq E_1$, f
is not a function from E_1 to E_1.

(3) Let E_1^+ be the set of all non-negative real numbers and $f' = \{(x,y); x \in E_1^+, y \in E_1, y = \sqrt{x}\}$. Now $\sqrt{x}$ means the principal
(non-negative) square root of x so we may conclude that f' is a func-
tion from E_1^+ into E_1. This follows from the fact that every non-negative real number has a unique, non-negative, real square root. Notice
that we might write $f': E_1^+ \longrightarrow E_1^+$ and have f' as an onto function,
but this only exemplifies the following obvious statement: a function
is always a function from its domain *onto* its range.

(4) Let C be the set of complex numbers and if $z \in C$, represent z as
$x + yi$ where x and y are elements of E_1 and $i = \sqrt{-1}$. Suppose
$f = \{(z,x); z \in C, x \in E_1 \text{ and } z = x + yi \text{ for some } y \in E_1\}$. Notice
that the image of z is the real part of z, namely x. Since every complex
number has a real part (perhaps zero), $\mathfrak{D}(f) = C$. Furthermore, if
(z,x) and (z,y) are elements of f, then $x = y$ because the real part of a
given complex number is unique. Therefore f is a function by Defini-

tion 3.11. Clearly, f is a function onto E_1, since every real number may be viewed as a complex number whose imaginary part is zero. But f is not 1–1 since $(3 + 2i, 3)$ and $(3 + i, 3)$ are elements of f yet $3 + 2i \neq 3 + i$.

(5) Let $f = \{(x,y); \; x \in E_1, \; y \in E_1, \; y = \sin x\}$. Sin x exists for every real number x by definition of sine, therefore $\mathfrak{D}(f) = E_1$. Moreover, the sine of any real number is unique. Therefore, f is a function from E_1 into E_1. We may easily show that f is not onto since there exists no $x \in E_1$ such that $\sin x = 2$ by definition of $\sin x$. Finally, we see that f is not 1–1 since $(\pi,0) \in f$ and $(2\pi,0) \in f$ and $\pi \neq 2\pi$.

· ·

Let $f \colon A \longrightarrow B$. Since f is a relation, f induces an inverse relation, f^{-1}, in accordance with Definition 3.6. Now f^{-1} may fail to be a function from B to A in two ways. First, it may happen that $\mathfrak{D}(f^{-1}) \neq B$. This will occur whenever $\mathfrak{R}(f) \neq B$, in other words, when f is not onto. Second, it may happen that f^{-1} fails to satisfy part (ii) of Definition 3.11. This occurs when f is a many-to-one function, implying that some of the elements of B would not have unique images under f^{-1}. Thus, whenever $f \colon A \longrightarrow B$ is not onto or is not 1–1 the inverse relation f^{-1} will not be a function from B to A.

· ·

DEFINITION 3.14

If $f \colon A \xrightarrow[\text{1-1}]{\text{onto}} B$, then the inverse relation, f^{-1}, from B to A will be called the *inverse function of f*.

· ·

An immediate consequence of Definition 3.14 is the next theorem.

· ·

THEOREM 3.3

Let A and B be sets. If $f \colon A \xrightarrow[\text{1-1}]{\text{onto}} B$, then $f^{-1} \colon B \xrightarrow[\text{1-1}]{\text{onto}} A$.

PROOF

Exercise 3.7–1.

. . . .

EXERCISES

1. Prove Theorem 3.3.

2. Which of the *functions* in Exercise 3.6–1 are onto and which are 1–1?

3. Which of the *functions* in Exercise 3.6–2 are onto and which are 1–1?

4. Which of the functions in the five examples at the end of Section 3.6 are onto and which are 1–1?

5. Decide which of the relations below are functions, which are onto, and which are 1–1, and then prove your assertions.

    a. $f = \{(x,y); x \in Z, y \in Z, y = 2x\}$.
    b. $g = \{(x,y); x \in E_1, y \in E_1, y = 4/(1 - x)\}$.
    c. $h = \{(x,y); x \in C, y \in C, y^3 = x\}$.
    d. $j = \{(x,y); x \in E_1, y \in E_1, y = 1$ if x is rational, $y = -1$ if x is irrational$\}$. (Try to sketch a graph of this relation.)
    e. $k = \{(x,y); x \in E_1, y \in E_1, y = |x|\}$.

6. Prove that the identity function I_A is 1–1 and onto.

3.8 BINARY OPERATIONS

In this section we will show an important way in which functions are used in mathematics. By way of illustration we will consider the subject of arithmetic and the fundamental operation called addition of natural numbers.

Consider the statement "$2 + 3 = 5$." Another way of expressing this fact is to say, "5 *is the sum of* 2 *and* 3." Notice that the ordered pair of natural numbers (2,3) is paired with the natural number 5 in this operation. In general, in the addition of natural numbers, any ordered pair of natural numbers (a,b) is paired with a third natural number, say c, and we say that c *is the sum of a and b*. Clearly, the ordered pair (a,b) is an element of the Cartesian product $N \times N$ where N is the set of natural numbers and c is an element of N. Since (a,b) is paired with C in this operation it follows that addition of natural numbers may be expressed as a relation from $N \times N$ to N. Thus, by using the symbol $+$ to represent this operation, $+ \subseteq (N \times N) \times N$ and $((2,3),5) \in +$. We will show that $+$ is a function from $N \times N$ to N.

For every ordered pair of natural numbers (a,b) there exists a natural number c which is called the sum of a and b; therefore, $\mathfrak{D}(+) = N \times N$, satisfying part (i) of Definition 3.11. Furthermore, if $((a,b),c) \in +$ and $((a,b),d) \in +$ then $c = a + b = d$ and $+$ satisfies part (ii) of Definition 3.11. Therefore, $+$ is a function from $N \times N$ to N, i.e., $+: N \times N \longrightarrow N$.

Similar remarks may be made concerning the operations of multiplication of natural numbers, subtraction of integers, and the like. Let us make a general definition of functions of this type.

. . . .

DEFINITION 3.15

If A is a set, then a function from $A \times A$ to A is called a *binary operation on A*.

. . . .

Symbolically, if $*$ is a binary operation on A, we write: $*: A \times A \longrightarrow A$.

Of course it is awkward to write "$((2,3),5) \in +$" so we usually write "$2 + 3 = 5$." In general, we usually write "$a * b = c$" instead of "$((a,b),c) \in *$." Incidentally, in those areas of mathematics, such as group theory, where a study of binary operations is essential, the fact that $\mathfrak{R}(*) \subseteq A$ is usually referred to as the *closure* property of the operation $*$.

. . . .

EXERCISES

1. Show that $+$, defined above, is not 1–1.

2. Prove that the relation $*$ defined below is a binary operation:
   $* = \{((x,y),z); x,y,z \in Z, z = x + y - 1\}$.

3. Show that the operation in Exercise 3.8–2 is not 1–1.

4. Is the operation in Exercise 3.8–2 an onto function? Can you explain why?

5. A *ternary operation* on set A is a function from $((A \times A) \times A)$ to A. Give some examples of ternary operations.

3.9 COMPOSITION OF FUNCTIONS

Suppose that $f: A \longrightarrow B$ and $g: B \longrightarrow C$ are functions. Let us define a set of ordered pairs as follows: $h = \{(x,z); x \in A, z \in C, z = g(f(x))\}$. The symbol "$z = g(f(x))$" deserves explanation. By Definition 3.12, $f(x)$ is the image of the element x of set A under the function f. Hence $f(x)$ is an element of set B or $f(x) \in \mathfrak{D}(g)$. Similarly $g(f(x))$ is the image of $f(x) \in B$ under the function g. Thus, $z = g(f(x))$ is the image of the image of x under the functions g and f, respectively. Now the set h is a function from A to C (see Theorem 3.4) and the image of $x \in A$ under the function h is $z \in C$. That is, $h(x) = z = g(f(x))$, which is to say that the image of x under the function h is the same as the image of the image of x under g and f, respectively. Consider the following examples of this general notion.

. . . .

EXAMPLES

(1) Let $A = \{1,2,3,4\}$, $B = \{a,b,c,d\}$, $C = \{p,q,r\}$,
   $f = \{(1,a), (2,c), (3,b), (4,a)\}$,
   and $g = \{(a,p), (b,p), (c,q), (d,q)\}$ and form h as above.

Then $h(1) = g(f(1)) = g(a) = p$ or $(1,p) \in h$.
$\quad\ h(2) = g(f(2)) = g(c) = q$ or $(2,q) \in h$.
$\quad\ h(3) = g(f(3)) = g(b) = p$ or $(3,p) \in h$.
$\quad\ h(4) = g(f(4)) = g(a) = p$ or $(4,p) \in h$.
Thus, $h = \{(1,p), (2,q), (3,p), (4,p)\}$.

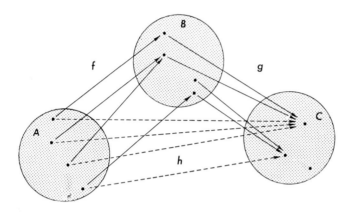

FIGURE 3.9 • A function h from A into C

(2) Let A, B and C be the sets of isolated dots in Figure 3.9 and the functions f and g be the ones indicated. Then the function h is shown by the use of dotted lines connecting the proper elements of A and C.

. . . .

The functions h in Examples 1 and 2 are the result of an operation on the functions f and g, and we will assign a name and symbol to functions like h in the next definition.

. . . .

DEFINITION 3.16

If $f: A \longrightarrow B$, and $g: B \longrightarrow C$, then the set h defined by $h = \{(x,z);$ $x \in A, z \in C$, and $\exists\ y \in B$ such that $y = f(x)$ and $z = g(y) = g(f(x))\}$, is called the *composition of g and f*, denoted $g \circ f$.

. . . .

Notice that to say $h(x) = z = g(f(x))$ is the same as to say that there exists $y \in B$ such that $(x,y) \in f$, $(y,z) \in g$ and $(x,z) \in h$.

. . . .

THEOREM 3.4

If f, g, and h are defined as in Definition 3.16, then $h = g \circ f$ is a function from A to C.

PROOF

By definition, $h = g \circ f$ is a subset of $A \times C$, therefore, $h = g \circ f$ is a relation from A to C and hence, $\mathfrak{D}(h) \subseteq A$.

Let $x \in A$. Since $\mathfrak{D}(f) = A$, $\exists\, y \in B$ such that $y = f(x)$. But $\mathfrak{D}(g) = B$ and since $y \in B\ \exists\ z \in C$ such that $z = g(y)$. Thus, $z = g(f(x))$ with $x \in A$ and $z \in C$ so that $z = h(x) = (g \circ f)(x)$. Hence $x \in \mathfrak{D}(h)$ and since x was chosen arbitrarily, $A \subseteq \mathfrak{D}(h)$. By Theorem 2.2, $\mathfrak{D}(h) = \mathfrak{D}(g \circ f) = A$, satisfying part (i) of Definition 3.11.

Suppose that $(x,z_1) \in h$ and $(x,z_2) \in h$. Then $\exists\ y_1 \in B$ and $y_2 \in B$ such that $y_1 = f(x)$ and $y_2 = f(x)$ where $g(y_1) = z_1$ and $g(y_2) = z_2$. Since f is a function, $y_1 = y_2$ and since g is a function, $z_1 = z_2$, satisfying part (ii) of Definition 3.11. Therefore, $h = g \circ f$ is a function from A to C.

Q.E.D.

. . . .

We have shown that the composition of the special functions g and f is another function. Notice that prerequisite to this composition we must have $\mathfrak{D}(g) \supseteq \mathfrak{R}(f)$. Except for this requirement we would have been able to call the composition of functions a binary operation on the set of all functions. However, we will show that composition of functions does have a property common to many binary operations, namely, associativity.

Before we come to the theorem, however, observe that the composition of functions is a function and remember that a function is a set. Hence, if we are asked to prove that two functions are equal, we will find Theorem 2.2 of great use.

. . . .

THEOREM 3.5

Composition of functions is associative. That is, if $f: A \longrightarrow B$, $g: B \longrightarrow C$, and $h: C \longrightarrow D$, then $h \circ (g \circ f) = (h \circ g) \circ f$.

PROOF

Let (u,v) be an element of $h \circ (g \circ f)$. Then $u \in A$, $v \in D$ and $\exists\, z \in C$ such that $(u,z) \in g \circ f$ and $(z,v) \in h$. But $(u,z) \in g \circ f$ implies $\exists\, y \in B$ such that $(u,y) \in f$ and $(y,z) \in g$. Then $(y,z) \in g$ and $(z,v) \in h$ implies $(y,v) \in h \circ g$ which, together with $(u,y) \in f$ implies $(u,v) \in (h \circ g) \circ f$. Hence, $h \circ (g \circ f) \subseteq (h \circ g) \circ f$.

In a similar manner it may be shown that $(h \circ g) \circ f \subseteq h \circ (g \circ f)$ and by Theorem 2.2 we conclude that $h \circ (g \circ f) = (h \circ g) \circ f$. Q.E.D.

An alternate proof of Theorem 3.5 may be given in the following way. Since $h \circ (g \circ f): A \longrightarrow D$ and $(h \circ g) \circ f: A \longrightarrow D$, we have $\mathfrak{D}(h \circ (g \circ f)) = A = \mathfrak{D}((h \circ g) \circ f)$ and thus all of the first coordinates of the function $h \circ (g \circ f)$ are the same as the first coordinates of the function $(h \circ g) \circ f$. Furthermore, for each $x \in A$, it follows that $(h \circ (g \circ f))(x) = h((g \circ f)(x)) = h(g(f(x))) = (h \circ g)(f(x)) = ((h \circ g) \circ f)(x)$. Hence, the image of each element of A is identical in both functions. Therefore, since every ordered pair in each function is the same as some ordered pair in the other, the two functions are equal by the Axiom of Extent.

The following is an example of the use of binary operations, composition of functions, and the identity function in the theory of groups.

Let A be a non-empty set and $\mathfrak{F} = \{f; f: A \xrightarrow[1-1]{\text{onto}} A\}$. Then if $f, g \in \mathfrak{F}, f \circ g: A \longrightarrow A$ and may be shown to be 1–1 and onto (see Exercise 3.9–1). Therefore, $f \circ g \in \mathfrak{F}$ and thus, $\circ: \mathfrak{F} \times \mathfrak{F} \longrightarrow \mathfrak{F}$, which is to say that $\circ$ is a binary operation on $\mathfrak{F}$. Also, $I_A: A \longrightarrow A$ is 1–1 and onto by Exercise 3.7–6, so $I_A \in \mathfrak{F}$. Moreover, as will be shown in Exercise 3.9–4, for every function $f \in \mathfrak{F}$, $f \circ I_A = I_A \circ f = f$. By Theorem 3.3, if $f \in \mathfrak{F}$, then $f^{-1} \colon A \longrightarrow A$ is 1–1 and onto so that $f^{-1} \in \mathfrak{F}$ and by Exercise 3.9–3, $f \circ f^{-1} = f^{-1} \circ f = I_A$. Finally, by Theorem 3.5, $f \circ (g \circ h) = (f \circ g) \circ h$. Summarizing these facts we have the following four properties of $\circ$ and $\mathfrak{F}$:

(i) $\circ \colon \mathfrak{F} \times \mathfrak{F} \longrightarrow \mathfrak{F}$.

(ii) $\exists\ I_A \in \mathfrak{F}$ such that $f \circ I_A = I_A \circ f = f$, $\forall f \in \mathfrak{F}$.

(iii) $\forall f \in \mathfrak{F}$, $\exists\ f^{-1} \in \mathfrak{F} \ni f \circ f^{-1} = f^{-1} \circ f = I_A$.

(iv) If f, g, $h \in \mathfrak{F}$, then $f \circ (g \circ h) = (f \circ g) \circ h$.

Any set with a binary operation satisfying (i)–(iv) is called a *group*. We write $(\mathfrak{F}, \circ)$, which is read "the group $\mathfrak{F}$," as an abbreviation for the fact that $\mathfrak{F}$, together with the binary operation $\circ$, forms a group. The members of $\mathfrak{F}$ are often called *transformations* and $\mathfrak{F}$ a group of transformations.

As another example, the system $(E_1, +)$ is a group since it satisfies the four properties.

(i) $+ \colon E_1 \times E_1 \longrightarrow E_1$.

(ii) $\exists\ 0 \in E_1$ such that $a + 0 = 0 + a = a$, $\forall\ a \in E_1$.

(iii) $\forall\ a \in E_1$, $\exists\ -a \in E_1$ such that $a + (-a) = (-a) + a = 0$.

(iv) If $a, b, c \in E_1$, then $a + (b + c) = (a + b) + c$.

. . . .

EXERCISES

1. If $f \colon A \longrightarrow B$ and $g \colon B \longrightarrow C$ and if both f and g are 1–1 and onto functions, prove that $g \circ f$ is 1–1 and onto.

2. If f and g are the 1–1 and onto functions of Exercise 3.9–1, prove that $(g \circ f)^{-1} = f^{-1} \circ g^{-1}$.

3. If $f: A \longrightarrow A$ is 1–1 and onto, we have shown in Theorem 3.3 that f^{-1} is 1–1 and onto. Show that $f \circ f^{-1} = f^{-1} \circ f = I_A$, the identity function in A.

4. If f is defined as in Exercise 3.9–3, show that $f \circ I_A = I_A \circ f = f$.

5. Prove that composition of functions is not commutative.

6. Which of the following are groups and which are not? State your reasons.

   a. $(E, +)$, where E is the set of even integers.
   b. $(E, \cdot)$, where $\cdot$ is ordinary multiplication.
   c. $(Z, -)$, where $-$ is ordinary subtraction.
   d. $(N, -)$, where N is the set of natural numbers.
   e. $(D, \cdot)$, where D is the set of odd integers.

7. Complete the proof of Theorem 3.5.

3.10   RESTRICTIONS OF FUNCTIONS

Given a certain function, say f, from A to B, it may be convenient and advantageous to form a subset of f which has properties not possessed by f. For instance, if f is onto but not 1–1, it may be desirable to form a subset of f which is still onto but also 1–1. Of course, the domain of this new relation will not be the same as the domain of f, nor will the relation be a function from A to B, but it may be considered to be a 1–1 function from some subset of A into B. In general, such a limiting of the domain of a function is called a *restriction* of the function. The following definition makes this concept explicit.

. . . .

DEFINITION 3.17

If f is a function from A to B and A' is a subset of A, then $\{(x,y);$ $(x,y) \in f$ and $x \in A'\}$, denoted $f \mid A'$, is called a *restriction of f to A'*.

. . . .

We sometimes read $f \mid A'$ as "f cut down to A'." It may be easily shown that $f \mid A'$ is a function from A' to B (see Exercise 3.10–1).

. . . .

DEFINITION 3.18

If f and g are functions and g is a restriction of f, then f is called an extension of g.

. . . .

EXAMPLES

(1) Let $A = \{a,b,c,d\}$, $B = \{1,2,3,4\}$ and $f = \{(a,1), (b,1), (c,2), (d,3)\}$. Some of the possible restrictions of f are:

(a) $f \mid C = \{(a,1), (b,1)\}$, where $C = \{a,b\} \subset A$.
(b) $f \mid D = \{(b,1), (c,2), (d,3)\}$, where $D = \{b,c,d\} \subset A$. Notice that $f \mid D: D \xrightarrow[1-1]{} B$ but is not onto.

(2) If A, B and f are as in Example (1), some of the possible extensions of f are:

(a) $\{(a,1), (b,1), (c,2), (d,3), (e,1)\}$. The domain of this function is a superset of A, namely $\{a,b,c,d,e\}$.
(b) $\{(a,1), (b,1), (c,2), (d,3), (e,2), (f,2), (g,2), (h,2)\}$. The domain of this function is $\{a,b,c,d,e,f,g,h\}$.

(3) Let $M = \{m,n,p,q,r\}$ and $N = \{1,2,3\}$. Then $t = \{(m,2), (n,3), (p,2), (q,1), (r,1)\}$ is a function from M onto N but is not 1–1. One of the restrictions of t which is 1–1 and onto is:

$$t \mid M' = \{(n,3), (p,2), (q,1)\}, \text{ where } M' = \{n,p,q\}.$$

Another restriction of t which is 1–1 and onto is:

$$t \mid M'' = \{(m,2), (n,3), (r,1)\}, \text{ where } M'' = \{m,n,r\}.$$

Clearly, there are two other restrictions of t which are 1–1 and onto.

. . . .

The examples show that there are as many restrictions of a function as there are subsets of its domain and that there are an unlimited number of extensions of a given function. The following exercises will point out other relationships which will prove of value in later developments.

. . . .

EXERCISES

1. If f is a function from A to B and $A' \subseteq A$, prove that $f \mid A'$ is a function from A' to B, and $f \mid A' \subseteq f$.

2. List the other restrictions which are possible in the function f of Example 1 above. Identify those that are 1–1. Can any of them be onto?

3. List the other two 1–1 and onto restrictions of function t of Example 3 above.

4. Prove that if a function f is not onto, no restriction of f is onto.

5. If $f: A \xrightarrow[1-1]{\text{onto}} B$ and $A' \subseteq A$, prove that $f \mid A'$ is a 1–1 function onto its range.

6. If $f: A \longrightarrow B$ and $g: B \longrightarrow C$ and $A' \subseteq A$, prove that $(g \circ f) \mid A' = g \circ (f \mid A')$.

7. Prove that if f is not 1–1, no extension of f is 1–1.

8. Prove that if a function f has n elements in its domain, then there are 2^n possible restrictions of f.

9. If $f: A \longrightarrow B$ and $A' \subseteq A$, then $\mathcal{R}(f \mid A') = f(A')$.

4

FINITE AND INFINITE SETS

4.1 INTRODUCTION

In Chapter 1 we indicated that the theory of sets was devised by Georg Cantor in an effort to systematize the study of the "infinite," a notion which had plagued mathematicians and philosophers alike for centuries. From the paradoxes of Zeno to the foundations of analysis, we find evidence of a need for a systematic treatment of the "infinite," and in 1895 Cantor made the first step toward answering that need.

The notions which we will formalize in this chapter may be motivated in the following way. We have used the word "finite" in connection with sets in a purely naive sense, relying on intuitive ideas of the reader. In this naive sense, a set is "finite" if we can systematically count the number of its elements and arrive at a stopping point in the process. Thus, we can associate a positive integer n with each "finite" set and in fact label its elements systematically using all positive integers from 1 to n inclusive as subscripts.

Continuing in the naive sense, an "infinite" set ought to be one in which this counting process can never end, i.e., ought to be a non-finite set. Thus, the set N of all natural numbers (or positive integers) would be an "infinite" set for we cannot conceive of a largest natural number and hence our counting process would never end. Likewise the set of all real numbers would be an "infinite" set. One of Cantor's greatest achievements was to show that it is possible to distinguish between certain "infinite" sets and thus, if each set corresponds to some number, the notion of counting is extended beyond the "finite." We proceed to develop these ideas formally in the sequel.

Often we have seen that knowledge of a property of "finite" sets provides insight into a property of sets in general. In fact, we have often chosen particular finite sets to illustrate a point and then followed up with the necessary theoretical structure to justify a general concept which was intuitively appealing. However, as the reader is aware, intuition can sometimes lead one astray, in which case complete reliance upon the theory is the only recourse. Therefore, as we move from a study of "finite" sets, which are particularly simple, to "infinite" sets, which are more complex, be on guard against a dependence on intuition, for in the final analysis all intuition must be tested using axioms, definitions, and theorems within the theory.

4.2 EQUIVALENCE OF SETS

Let us denote by N_k, the set of all natural numbers from 1 to k inclusive, i.e., $N_k = \{1, 2, \ldots, k\}$.* For each natural number k,

---

* We follow the notation used by Wilder. Raymond L. Wilder, *The Foundations of Mathematics* (New York: John Wiley and Sons, Inc., 1958).

N_k is a well-defined set. In ordinary counting everyone would agree that we should say N_k has exactly k elements. Such sets will serve well to define "finite" sets.

. . . .

DEFINITION 4.1

Let A be a set. A is *finite* if either A is empty or there is a natural number k and a 1–1 function f mapping A onto N_k. A is *infinite* if it is not finite.

. . . .

Of course, if $f\colon A \longrightarrow N_k$ is a 1–1 correspondence, then $f^{-1}\colon N_k \longrightarrow A$ exists and is a 1–1 correspondence. Hence, which set we use for the domain is immaterial. Also we should observe that the definition of infinite, as is so often the case with negative definitions of that type, is not a very useful one. Thus, to establish that A is infinite would require us to show that we cannot find a natural number k and a 1–1 correspondence f such that $f\colon A \longrightarrow N_k$. Such a task seems rather overwhelming at this point. We shall be interested in stating an equivalent but more useful definition later but defer this for the time being.

Now suppose that A and B are finite sets. Further, suppose that $f\colon A \xrightarrow[1-1]{\text{onto}} N_k$ and $g\colon B \xrightarrow[1-1]{\text{onto}} N_k$ in accordance with Definition 4.1. Then, we would certainly say that A and B are equivalent in the sense that they both have k elements. Indeed, if we let $h = g^{-1} \circ f$, then $h\colon A \longrightarrow B$ and it is readily verified that h is 1–1 and onto, i.e., a 1–1 correspondence. This prompts us to define the notion of equivalence for arbitrary sets.

. . . .

DEFINITION 4.2

Let A and B be sets. Then A and B are *equivalent* (or *equipollent*, or have the same *power*) symbolized $A \sim B$, if there exists a 1–1 correspondence f such that $f\colon A \longrightarrow B$.

. . . .

THEOREM 4.1

Let $\mathcal{C}$ be a non-empty set of sets. Further, define $r = \{(A,B)$; $A \in \mathcal{C}, B \in \mathcal{C}, A \sim B\}$. Then, r is an equivalence relation in $\mathcal{C}$.

PROOF

Clearly, $r \subseteq \mathcal{C} \times \mathcal{C}$. Let $A \in \mathcal{C}$ and consider I_A, the identity relation in A. We know that $I_A \colon A \xrightarrow[1-1]{\text{onto}} A$ by Exercise 3.7–6. Hence, $A \sim A$ by Definition 4.2 so that $(A,A) \in r$. Since A was chosen arbitrarily, it follows that r is reflexive.

Suppose A and B are elements of $\mathcal{C}$ with $(A,B) \in r$. Then, $\exists f \colon A \xrightarrow[1-1]{\text{onto}} B$ since $A \sim B$. But $f^{-1} \colon B \xrightarrow[1-1]{\text{onto}} A$ by Theorem 3.3; hence, $B \sim A$ by Definition 4.2 so that $(B,A) \in r$. Therefore, r is symmetric.

Finally, if $A,B,C \in \mathcal{C}$ with $(A,B) \in r$ and $(B,C) \in r$, then $A \sim B$ and $B \sim C$ so that $\exists f \colon A \xrightarrow[1-1]{\text{onto}} B$ and $\exists g \colon B \xrightarrow[1-1]{\text{onto}} C$. It follows from Exercise 3.9–1 that $g \circ f \colon A \xrightarrow[1-1]{\text{onto}} C$ so that $A \sim C$ by Definition 4.2. Thus $(A,C) \in r$ and r is transitive.

Since r is reflexive, symmetric, and transitive, r is an equivalence relation as asserted.   Q.E.D.

. . . .

From the preceding theorem the reader can see why we used the term "equivalent" in connection with Definition 4.2. Also, it should be noticed that Definition 4.1 may be rephrased quite simply by saying A is finite if $A \sim N_k$ for some natural number k.

. . . .

EXERCISES

1. If A and B are finite sets and $f \colon A \xrightarrow[1-1]{\text{onto}} N_k$ and $g \colon B \xrightarrow[1-1]{\text{onto}} N_k$, prove that $h = g^{-1} \circ f \colon A \xrightarrow[1-1]{\text{onto}} B$.

2. If $A = \{a,b,c,d,e\}$ and $B = \{v,w,x,y,z\}$, in how many ways may it be shown that $A \sim B$? (Hint: How many 1–1 correspondences exist between A and B?)

3. If $A \sim N_k$ and $B \sim N_k$, how many 1–1 correspondences exist between A and B?

4. Let $A = N_7$. The following functions have A as a subset of their domains. Which functions restricted to A have a range which is equivalent to A?

$$f = \{(x,y); x \in E_1, y \in E_1, y = 2x + 1\}.$$
$$g = \{(x,y); x \in N, y \in N, y = x^2\}.$$
$$h = \{(x,y); x \in Z, y \in Z, y = 3^x\}.$$
$$j = \{(x,y); x \in E_1, y \in E_1, y = \sin x\}.$$
$$k = \{(x,y); x \in E_1, y \in C, y = 3x - 2i\}.$$
$$m = \{(x,y); x \in E_1^\dagger, y \in E_1, y = \log_7 x\}.$$

5. Give a function from $A = \{1,2,3,4,5,6,7,8,9,10\}$ which is 1–1 onto $B = \{1,4,7,10,13,16,19,22,25,28\}$; from A 1–1 onto $C = \{0,7,27,63, \ldots, 999\}$.

4.3 INFINITE SETS

We have introduced the term infinite in a very specific way in the preceding section, namely, to denote a set which is not finite. It is now time to examine the structure of such sets more closely and to find a more constructive but equivalent definition of infinite. In so doing we will see a motivation for defining the concept of cardinal number which will follow in the next chapter.

It seems almost too trivial to mention that none of our sets N_k can be equivalent to a proper subset of itself. We know that in order for such to be true it is necessary to pair the elements of N_k in a 1–1 fashion with a subset of itself. The old maxim "The whole is greater than any of its parts" seems to apply quite well. A formal proof of this obvious fact is not difficult but does involve more detail than we care to insert at this point. The interested reader is referred to the appendix.

Now the above property must hold for arbitrary finite sets also. Thus, if B is finite and non-empty then $B \sim N_k$ for some natural number k under, say, the 1–1 correspondence ψ. Let A be a proper subset of B and suppose that $A \sim B$. Now let $C = \psi(A)$. Then $C \subseteq N_k$ and $\exists\ b_0 \in B$ such that $b_0 \notin A$ so that $\psi(b_0) \notin C$ while $\psi(b_0) \in N_k \Rightarrow C \subset N_k$. Finally, $A \sim C$ under the 1–1 correspondence $\psi \mid A$ whence $N_k \sim C$, a proper subset of itself. Since this is absurd we may say that no finite set can be equivalent to one of its proper subsets, and this is a fundamental characterization of finite sets.

Consider the set N of natural numbers and let E be the set of even natural numbers; i.e., $E = \{2,4,6, \ldots\}$. Let $f\colon N \longrightarrow E$ be defined by $f(x) = 2x\ \forall\ x \in N$. It is easily verified that f is a 1–1 correspondence and hence $N \sim E$. But E is a proper subset of N! Here, contrary to the finite case, the maxim, "The whole is greater than any of its parts," does not apply at all when the criterion of equivalence is used. Thus, N must be an infinite set, for if it were finite it could not have this property as pointed out above. It would thus appear that the difficult task, mentioned above, of proving a set is infinite may be accomplished using this criterion.

This is precisely the way Dedekind defined infinite set; i.e., a set A is (Dedekind) infinite if there is a set B such that $B \subset A$ and $A \sim B$. A set is (Dedekind) finite if it is not (Dedekind) infinite. We see from the above that any set that is (Dedekind) infinite is infinite in the sense of our definition. Is the converse true? As a matter of fact the two definitions are equivalent but we consider the proof outside the realm of the present course.* Henceforth, we will not distinguish between the two definitions.

In summary, finite sets are sets which are equivalent to some set N_k and we may say such sets have exactly k elements. An infinite set, on the other hand, cannot be equivalent to any set N_k and is always equivalent to at least one of its proper subsets. What can we say about the number of its elements? For example, we are sorely tempted to say that N and E (given above) have the same

---

* For an excellent discussion of this and related matters, see Raymond L. Wilder, *The Foundations of Mathematics* (New York: John Wiley and Sons, Inc., 1958), Chapter III.

number of elements since they are equivalent. On the other hand, intuition dictates that we should say N has more elements than E since the latter is a proper subset of the former. This shows that for infinite sets we cannot rely entirely on our intuition and we shall have to make some suitable definition of what we mean by the number of elements of an infinite set. Before doing so, however, it is necessary to examine the structure of infinite sets further.

We close this section with a theorem which summarizes equivalence for finite and infinite sets and will be useful in what follows.

. . . .

THEOREM 4.2

If $A \sim B$ and B is infinite (finite) then A is also infinite (finite).

PROOF

Suppose $A \sim B$ and B is infinite. Then $\exists\, B_0 \subset B$ such that $B_0 \sim B$. Let $\psi\colon B \xrightarrow[1\text{-}1]{\text{onto}} A$ be a 1–1 correspondence between A and B. Letting $A_0 = \psi(B_0)$ we have $A_0 \subset A$ and $A_0 \sim B_0$ under $\psi \mid B_0$. Then, by transitivity, $A_0 \sim B$ so that $A_0 \sim A$ and hence A is infinite.

Suppose $A \sim B$ and B is finite. Then, if A were infinite we have by symmetry $B \sim A$ so B would be infinite as above contrary to the assumption. Thus A must be finite also.   Q.E.D.

. . . .

EXERCISE

1. Verify that $f\colon N \longrightarrow E$ defined by $f(x) = 2x \; \forall \; x \in N$ is a 1–1 correspondence. (E is the set of even, natural numbers.)

4.4 DENUMERABLE SETS

Thinking of the various sets N_k as k increases, it would appear that the first infinite set we should examine closely is the set N of all natural numbers. We have indicated that N is infinite. Also,

because of Theorem 4.2, we might expect that sets which are equivalent to N should have some common properties. This prompts
the next definition.

. . . .

DEFINITION 4.3

A set A is *denumerable* if $A \sim N$. A set A is *countable* if A is finite
or denumerable.

. . . .

The reasons for introducing the words used in Definition 4.2
are not yet too apparent. Although the set N is infinite we can, at
least in spirit, "count" its elements because of its special nature.
Of course in practice this can never be accomplished because the
natural numbers, taken in order, have no last element. But we
will soon have sets that do not possess even this much simplicity
so we reserve a special name for sets equivalent to N. Thus, the
word countable would imply that we are able to count the elements
of the set involved. For finite sets there is no problem of counting
and the term is suitable. For denumerable sets we are stretching
the usual meaning slightly.

A word or two about notation. Suppose A is a finite set so
that $N_k \sim A$ under some 1–1 correspondence φ. It follows that
$A = \{\varphi(1), \varphi(2), \ldots, \varphi(k)\}$ for $\varphi(m)$ is a definite and distinct member of A for each $m \in \{1, 2, \ldots, k\} = N_k$. Since this is so, we will
denote $\varphi(m)$ by a_m to remind us that $\varphi(m) \in A$ and we will write
$A = \{a_1, a_2, \ldots, a_k\}$. Similarly, if A is denumerable so that
$N \sim A$ under the mapping φ, say, then for each $n \in N$ there is a
unique $a \in A$ such that $\varphi(n) = a$. We denote this unique element
of A by a_n to show the dependence on n and we write
$A = \{a_1, a_2, a_3, \ldots\}$ symbolically to denote a denumerable set.
Of course we cannot enclose all of the elements of A in braces so
the three dots are used to indicate that the elements are to be
thought of as being written in a definite order as indicated by the
subscripts. Also, since $\varphi: N \longrightarrow A$ is 1–1, we know that $a_i \neq a_j$

whenever $i \neq j$. Hence, whenever this technique is used to display the elements of a countable set we will always assume that the elements listed are all distinct.

Caution! The labeling of the elements of A as given above should not be confused with a sequence. Thus, the sequence $a_1, a_2, a_3, \ldots$ in which $a_n = 1$ for all n is the well-defined sequence $1,1,1, \ldots$ whereas $\{a_1, a_2, a_3, \ldots\} = \{1\}$. We may think of the elements of any denumerable set as constituting a sequence of distinct elements, but an arbitrary sequence will not necessarily determine a denumerable set as the above example shows.

We now proceed to prove several theorems that will characterize denumerable sets in general and will be quite useful for finding special examples of denumerable sets.

. . . .

THEOREM 4.3

If A is denumerable and $B \subseteq A$ then B is either finite or denumerable.

PROOF

Let $A = \{a_1, a_2, a_3, \ldots\}$. If $B = \emptyset$, then B is finite. Otherwise let n_1 be the smallest subscript for which $a_{n_1} \in B$ (the most extreme case being $n_1 = 1$). Let n_2 be the smallest subscript (if one exists) for which $a_{n_2} \in B - \{a_{n_1}\}$. Having so defined $a_{n_{k-1}}$, let a_{n_k} be the smallest subscript for which $a_{n_k} \in B - \{a_{n_1}, a_{n_2}, \ldots, a_{n_{k-1}}\}$. Now, it may happen that for some integer k, $B - \{a_{n_1}, a_{n_2}, \ldots, a_{n_{k-1}}\} = \emptyset$ in which case $B = \{a_{n_1}, a_{n_2}, \ldots a_{n_{k-1}}\}$ is finite. If this does not happen, then for every natural number k there exists $a_{n_k} \in A$ for which $a_{n_k} \in B$ so that $B \sim N$ under the correspondence $\varphi(a_{n_k}) = k$ so that B is denumerable. Q.E.D.

. . . .

THEOREM 4.4

If A is finite and $B \subseteq A$, then B is finite.

PROOF

Suppose B is infinite. Then $B \neq \emptyset$ and $B \neq A$. Also, $\exists\, C \subset B \ni B \sim C$ under the function f, say. Let $D = A - B$. Since $B \neq A$, $D \neq \emptyset$ and $A = B \cup D$ with $B \cap D = \emptyset$. Let us define

$$g(x) = \begin{cases} f(x) & \text{if } x \in B \\ x & \text{if } x \in D \end{cases}$$

Then, since $A = B \cup D$ and $f: B \xrightarrow[1-1]{onto} C$, we have $g: A \longrightarrow C \cup D$.

To show g is 1–1, let $x_1, x_2 \in A$ with $x_1 \neq x_2$. Three cases arise.

CASE 1

$x_1, x_2 \in B$. Then $g(x_1) = f(x_1) \neq f(x_2) = g(x_2)$ since f is 1–1.

CASE 2

$x_1, x_2 \in D$. Then $g(x_1) = x_1 \neq x_2 = g(x_2)$.

CASE 3

$x_1 \in B$, $x_2 \in D$. If $g(x_1) = g(x_2)$, then $f(x_1) = x_2 \Rightarrow x_2 \in C$ so that $x_2 \in C \cap D$ which is absurd since $C \cap D = \varnothing$. Thus, $g(x_1) \neq g(x_2)$.

Hence, g is 1–1.

To verify that g is onto, let $y \in C \cup D$. If $y \in C$, $\exists\ x \in B \ni f(x) = y$ whence $g(x) = f(x) = y$. If $y \in D$, let $x = y$. Then $x \in D$ and $g(x) = x = y$. In both cases, $x \in A$ and $g(x) = y$ so g is onto.

Since g is onto and 1–1, $A \sim C \cup D$ whereas $C \cup D \subset A$ so that A is infinite contrary to the hypothesis. Therefore, B is finite as asserted.   Q.E.D.

· ·

THEOREM 4.5

Suppose A is a finite set and B is a denumerable set. Then $A \cup B$ is denumerable.

PROOF

Let $C = A - B$. If $C = \varnothing$ then $A \subset B$ so that $A \cup B = B$ and hence $A \cup B \sim B$, i.e., $A \cup B$ is denumerable. If $C \neq \varnothing$, then $C \subseteq A$ and hence is finite by Theorem 4.4 so that $C \sim N_k$ for some k under f, say, and $B \sim N$ under g, say.

$$\text{Define } h(x) = \begin{cases} f(x) & \text{if } x \in C \\ g(x) + k & \text{if } x \in B \end{cases}$$

Then $h: C \cup B \longrightarrow N$ and is easily verified to be a 1–1 correspondence. Hence, $C \cup B$ is denumerable. But $A \cup B = C \cup B$ for

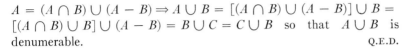

$A = (A \cap B) \cup (A - B) \Rightarrow A \cup B = [(A \cap B) \cup (A - B)] \cup B =$
$[(A \cap B) \cup B] \cup (A - B) = B \cup C = C \cup B$ so that $A \cup B$ is
denumerable.   Q.E.D.

. . . .

THEOREM 4.6

Let A and B be denumerable sets. Then $A \cup B$ is denumerable.

PROOF, CASE 1

$A \cap B = \varnothing$. Let D be the set of odd positive integers and E the
set of even positive integers. Both D and E are denumerable. By
hypothesis $A \sim N$ while $N \sim D$ so that $A \sim D$. Let f be a 1–1 correspondence between A and D. Similarly, let g be a 1–1 correspondence
between B and E. As above define

$$h(x) = \begin{cases} f(x) & \text{if } x \in A \\ g(x) & \text{if } x \in B \end{cases}$$

Then $h: A \cup B \longrightarrow N$. The reader may verify that h is 1–1, onto.
(Observe that $A \cap B = \varnothing$ is critical in the definition of h.)

CASE 2

$A \cap B \neq \varnothing$. Let $C = A - B$ so that $C \subseteq A$ and as before $A \cup B$
$= C \cup B$ with $C \cap B = \varnothing$. Now, by Theorem 4.3, C is finite or denumerable. If C is finite, then $C \cup B = A \cup B$ is denumerable by
Theorem 4.5, whereas if C is denumerable, then $C \cup B = A \cup B$ is denumerable by Case 1.

Thus, $A \cup B$ is denumerable in either case.   Q.E.D.

. . . .

COROLLARY

If $A_1, A_2, \ldots, A_n$ are each denumerable sets, then $\bigcup\limits_{i=1}^{n} A_i$ is denumerable.

PROOF

Left to the reader. Use mathematical induction and the theorem.

. . . .

We will often need a means of checking certain sets for denumerability beyond the use of Definition 4.3. A very useful tool for such a check is given by the following theorem.

. . . .

THEOREM 4.7

$N \times N$ is denumerable.

PROOF

Consider the array

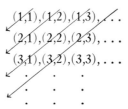

Clearly every one of the distinct elements (p,q), where p and q are natural numbers, is located in the array. Define $f: N \times N \longrightarrow N$ by the formula

$$f((p,q)) = \tfrac{1}{2}(p + q - 2)(p + q - 1) + p.$$

The definition is motivated by the following:

1. Agree to "count" by the diagonal procedure indicated by the arrows above. We would like $f((p,q))$ to be the integer that locates the position of (p,q) in the counting process.
2. Now each diagonal has a finite number of elements, contains one more element than the preceding diagonal, and has the property that each element of the diagonal is invariant under the sum of the coordinates p and q. Thus, if (p,q) and (m,n) are in the same diagonal, then $p + q = m + n$. Call $p + q$ the *index* of the diagonal.
3. Next observe that if the diagonal has index $p + q$, there are $p + q - 1$ elements in the diagonal.
4. Now in order to count to (p,q) first locate the diagonal in which it lies by the index $p + q$. In that diagonal, it is the pth element (located by counting first coordinates). Then, to arrive at the diagonal having index $p + q$ we would have counted all the elements in the $p + q - 2$ preceding diagonals for a total of $\tfrac{1}{2}(p + q - 2)(p + q - 1)$

elements. Hence, (p,q) is the $(\frac{1}{2}(p + q - 2)(p + q - 1) + p)^{\text{th}}$ element.

We next assert that $f: N \times N \longrightarrow N$ is 1–1 and onto. We first show that f is 1–1.

Suppose $(p,q) \neq (m,n)$. Then $p \neq m$ or $q \neq n$.

CASE 1

$p + q = m + n$. Then $p \neq m$ for if $p = m$, $p + q = m + n = p + n \Rightarrow q = n \Rightarrow (p,q) = (m,n)$ contrary to the assumption. Hence, $f((p,q)) = \frac{1}{2}(p + q - 2)(p + q - 1) + p = \frac{1}{2}(m + n - 2)(m + n - 1) + p \neq \frac{1}{2}(m + n - 2)(m + n - 1) + m = f((m,n))$.

CASE 2

$p + q \neq m + n$. Assume without loss of generality $p + q > m + n > 0$ so that $p + q \geq m + n + 1$. Now $p + q - 2 \geq m + n - 1 > 0$ and $p + q - 1 \geq m + n > 0$ so that $(p + q - 2)(p + q - 1) \geq (m + n - 1)(p + q - 1) \geq (m + n - 1)(m + n)$. Also, $f((p,q)) = \frac{1}{2}(p + q - 2)(p + q - 1) + p > \frac{1}{2}(p + q - 2)(p + q - 1) \geq \frac{1}{2}(m + n - 1)(m + n) \geq \frac{1}{2}(m + n - 1)(m + n) - n + 1 = \frac{1}{2}(m + n - 1)(m + n - 2 + 2) - n + 1 = \frac{1}{2}(m + n - 1)(m + n - 2) + m = f((m,n))$.

Hence, if $(p,q) \neq (m,n)$, then $f((p,q)) \neq f((m,n)) \Rightarrow f$ is 1–1.

Next we prove that f is onto. Given $n \in N$, $\exists\ k \in N \ni \frac{1}{2}k(k + 1) \leq n < \frac{1}{2}(k + 1)(k + 2)$.

CASE 1: $n = k(k + 1)/2$

Let $p = k$, $q = 1$. Then $f((p,q)) = f((k,1)) = \frac{1}{2}(k - 1)(k) + k = \frac{1}{2}k(k + 1) = n$.

CASE 2: $\frac{1}{2}k(k + 1) < n < \frac{1}{2}(k + 1)(k + 2)$

Let $p = n - \frac{1}{2}k(k + 1)$, $q = \frac{1}{2}(k + 1)(k + 2) - n + 1$, so that $p + q = \frac{1}{2}(k + 1)(k + 2) - \frac{1}{2}k(k + 1) + 1 = [1 + \ldots + k + (k + 1)] - [1 + \ldots + k] + 1 = k + 1 + 1 = k + 2$.* Now $p + q - 2 = k$ and $p + q - 1 = k + 1$ so that $f((p,q)) = \frac{1}{2}k(k + 1) + n - \frac{1}{2}k(k + 1) = n$.

Thus, in either case $\exists\ (p,q) \in N \times N$ such that $f((p,q)) = n$ and, since n was an arbitrary element of N, f is onto.

---

* Recall that $1 + 2 + \ldots + m = \frac{1}{2}m(m + 1) \ \forall\ m \in N$.

Since f is 1–1 and onto, f is a 1–1 correspondence and $N \times N \sim N$ by Definition 4.2.   Q.E.D.

. . . .

Theorem 4.6 and its corollary have exact counterparts if the word denumerable is replaced by the word finite. The proofs are quite similar to those of the theorem and its corollary and will be left to the reader as Exercises 4.4–2 and 4.4–3. If we combine Theorem 4.6 and its corollary with these two exercises, we may prove that the union of a finite number of sets, each of which is finite or denumerable, is itself finite or denumerable, respectively. (By the phrase "a finite number of sets," we mean that there is a set for each of the positive integers 1, 2, . . . , n for some positive integer n.) A quite extensive statement is given in Theorem 4.8 wherein the reader will notice the important role of Theorem 4.7.

. . . .

THEOREM 4.8

Let A_n be a denumerable set for each positive integer n with $A_n \cap A_m = \emptyset$ if $n \neq m$. Then $\bigcup_{n \in N} A_n$ is denumerable.

PROOF

It is instructive to first display the elements of each of the given sets as follows:

$$A_1 = \{a_{11}, a_{12}, a_{13}, \ldots\}$$
$$A_2 = \{a_{21}, a_{22}, a_{23}, \ldots\}$$
$$\vdots$$
$$A_n = \{a_{n1}, a_{n2}, a_{n3}, \ldots\}$$
$$\vdots$$

In this case our notation has the following significance: a_{ij} refers to the jth element in set A_i. Also, our requirement $A_n \cap A_m = \emptyset$ if $m \neq n$ assures us that $a_{ij} = a_{km} \Leftrightarrow i = k$ and $j = m$.

Let $A = \bigcup_{n \in N} A_n$ and define $f(a_{ij}) = (i,j)$ for each $i \in N$ and $j \in N$.
Then $f: A \longrightarrow N \times N$ and the reader may verify that f is 1–1 and onto.
Thus, $A \sim N \times N$ and $N \times N \sim N$ by Theorem 4.7, so that $A \sim N$ and
hence $A = \bigcup_{n \in N} A_n$ is denumerable as asserted.   Q.E.D.

. . . .

COROLLARY

If A_n is a non-empty finite set for each positive integer n and $A_n \cap A_m = \emptyset$ if $n \neq m$, then $\bigcup_{n \in N} A_n$ is denumerable.

PROOF

Let A_n' be a denumerable set for each n with $A_n' \cap A_m' = \emptyset$ if $n \neq m$
and $A_n' \cap A_m = \emptyset$ for all n and m (certainly such sets may be selected).*
Let $B_n = A_n \cup A_n'$ for each n. The sets B_n are denumerable by Theorem 4.5 and satisfy the conditions of the present theorem. Hence,
$\bigcup_{n \in N} B_n$ is denumerable and $\bigcup_{n \in N} A_n \subset \bigcup_{n \in N} B_n$ with $\bigcup_{n \in N} A_n$ clearly
infinite hence denumerable by Theorem 4.3.   Q.E.D.

. . . .

We have required in the theorem and its corollary that
$A_n \cap A_m = \emptyset$ for $n \neq m$ to insure that all of the elements considered are distinct. Actually this is much stronger than needed, but it is in the form we wish to have for applying it later. In the theorem, for instance, we might have $A_n = A_1$ for $n = 2, 3, 4, \ldots$
in which case $\bigcup_{n \in N} A_n = A_1$ which is denumerable. This would be
extreme. The reason we impose distinctness on our elements is so that f, defined in the proof, will be a function. For example, if
$a_{23} = a_{79}$, we would have $f(a_{23}) = (2,3)$ and $f(a_{23}) = f(a_{79}) = (7,9)$
so that f would not be a function. Nevertheless, the condition could be relaxed and the conclusion still hold.
In the finite case, as stated in the corollary, matters are much more delicate. For example, if $A_1 = \{0\}$ and $A_n = A_1$ for $n = 2, 3, \ldots$, then $\bigcup_{n \in N} A_n = A_1$ is certainly not denumerable but

———————————
* Let $A_n' = \{(a_{n,k}); k = 1, 2, 3, \ldots, a_n \in A_n\}$.

finite. This shows that a certain degree of caution must be exercised in drawing conclusions. A general statement that summarizes all of the above cases may be made, however. Thus, if A_n is a countable set for every positive integer n, then $\bigcup\limits_{n \in N} A_n$ is countable.

· ·

EXERCISES

1. Prove the corollary of Theorem 4.6.

2. Prove the counterpart to Theorem 4.6 wherein "denumerable" is replaced by "finite."

3. Prove the counterpart to the corollary of Theorem 4.6 wherein "denumerable" is replaced by "finite."

4. Prove that the function $f\colon A \longrightarrow N \times N$ in Theorem 4.8 is 1–1 and onto.

4.5 EXAMPLES OF DENUMERABLE SETS

We are now ready to give specific examples of denumerable sets utilizing various theorems of Section 4.4. The simplest (in a sense) denumerable set is the set N of natural numbers. Indeed, we have used N to define denumerability. It has served as a sort of standard against which sets are compared to test for denumerability. Many subsets of N are also denumerable. Thus, the set E of even natural numbers and the set D of odd natural numbers are each denumerable under the 1–1 mappings $f(n) = 2n$ and $g(n) = 2n - 1$ respectively. The mapping $h(n) = 10n$ with domain N is 1–1 and onto the set $\{10,20,30,40, \ldots\}$, which shows that the latter is denumerable. Again, if $\varphi(n) = n^2 \; \forall \; n \in N$ then φ is a 1–1 correspondence between N and its proper subset $\{1,4,9,16, \ldots\}$, the set of perfect squares of natural numbers. The reader may discover many more proper subsets of N that are denumerable.

There are also sets which contain N as a proper subset and still are denumerable. For example, let M be the set of negative integers and define $f(m) = -m \ \forall \ m \in M$. Now $-m \in N$ and f is clearly 1–1 and maps M onto N. Hence M is denumerable. Now let Z denote the set of all integers (positive, negative, and zero). Then $Z = M \cup \{0\} \cup N$ in which case Z is denumerable by applying Theorems 4.5 and 4.6.

Let us define a *fraction* as a ratio of two integers m/n with $n > 0$. The fraction is positive if $m > 0$ and negative if $m < 0$. We define the two fractions m/n and p/q as unequal if $m \neq p$ or $n \neq q$. In Theorem 4.8 let $a_{nm} = m/n$ whenever $m > 0$, $n > 0$ and $A_n = \{a_{n1}, a_{n2}, \ldots\} = \{1/n, 2/n, \ldots\}$ for $n = 1, 2, 3, \ldots$. Then, the conditions of Theorem 4.8 are fulfilled and we conclude that $\bigcup_{n \in N} A_n$ is denumerable. Letting F^+ denote the set of positive fractions, we see that $F^+ = \bigcup_{n \in N} A_n$ and is denumerable. If we let F^- denote the set of negative fractions, the 1–1 function $f(x) = -x$, maps F^- onto F^+ so that F^- is denumerable. Finally, the set $Q = \{\frac{0}{1}, \frac{0}{2}, \frac{0}{3}, \ldots\}$ is clearly denumerable and the set F of all fractions satisfies $F = F^+ \cup Q \cup F^-$ so is denumerable.

If we wish to represent certain distances on a line (having an origin and unit length) by fractions, we would discover that the fractions $\frac{1}{2}$ and $\frac{2}{4}$, for example, would represent the same point. This prompts the definition of rational number as follows. We will say that two fractions m/n and p/q are *equivalent* if $mq = np$, i.e., $m/n \sim p/q \Leftrightarrow mq = np$. We leave it to the reader to verify that $\sim$ defines an equivalence relation in F. Using our partition theorem (3.2) F is split into equivalence classes. Let us represent each equivalence class consisting of positive fractions by that member p/q in which p and q are relatively prime (have no common factors other than 1). Such a fraction is defined to be a positive *rational number*. Thus, for example, $\frac{1}{2}$ is the positive rational number representing the equivalence class $\{\frac{1}{2}, \frac{2}{4}, \frac{3}{6}, \ldots\}$. Let R^+ denote the set of positive rational numbers. Clearly R^+ is infinite and $R^+ \subset F^+$ so that R^+ is denumerable by Theorem 4.3. Next, we define the negative rational number p/q to be that member of the equivalence class of negative fractions such that $-p$ and q are relatively prime (remember p is negative if p/q is a negative fraction). Call the set of all these negative rational numbers R^-. Finally, define the rational number 0 to be the class $\{\frac{0}{1}, \frac{0}{2}, \frac{0}{3}, \ldots\}$. As before, R^- is denumerable and since R, the set of all rational numbers, is equal to $R^+ \cup \{0\} \cup R^-$, it follows that R is denumerable by Theorems 4.5 and 4.6.

Incidentally, it may be shown (see Exercise 4.5–2) that N is equivalent to a proper subset of R^+, namely $\{\frac{1}{1}, \frac{2}{1}, \frac{3}{1}, \ldots\} = N'$. Now, since N' is a proper subset of R and $N \sim N'$, it would seem that there are more positive rational numbers than there are natural numbers (in a naive sense, at least). However, N and R are both denumerable, hence, $N \sim R^+$. Thus, although our intuition indicates otherwise, the fact is that N and R^+ are equivalent sets.

We have seen that the set of rational numbers is denumerable. But even the set of rational numbers between 0 and 1 is denumerable. Letting that set be denoted by A, we have $A \subset R$, yet A is infinite for $\{\frac{1}{2}, \frac{1}{3}, \frac{1}{4}, \ldots\} \subset A$ so that A is denumerable by Theorem 4.3. Consequently, it must be possible to write the members of A in terms of a sequence as $A = \{r_1, r_2, r_3, \ldots\}$. But what sequence? Certainly not according to size, for then we would never know what to label r_1; that is to say, there is no first positive rational number for if $r > 0$ then $0 < r/2 < r$ and $r/2$ is again rational. One such enumeration would be to order first according to denominators then according to numerators, keeping in mind that numerator must be less than denominator. Thus, the first few elements would be $\{\frac{1}{2}, \frac{1}{3}, \frac{2}{3}, \frac{1}{4}, \frac{3}{4}, \frac{1}{5}, \frac{2}{5}, \frac{3}{5}, \frac{4}{5}, \frac{1}{6}, \frac{5}{6}, \ldots\}$. In this way, having ultimately accounted for each denominator and ordering the finite number of numerators for each denominator, we would certainly exhaust all rational numbers between 0 and 1.

Finally, we note that there are many other denumerable sets of interest; however, the explicit function which establishes the 1–1 correspondence may not be as simple as those in the preceding discussions. One of these sets is the set of all prime numbers $P =$

$\{2,3,5,7,\ldots\}$. Long ago Euclid proved that P is infinite. We prove that P is infinite by an indirect proof in the following way. Assume P is finite, say $P = \{2,3,5,\ldots,p_n\}$, where p_n is the largest prime. Now every natural number greater than 1 has a unique factorization into prime factors and hence is divisible by some prime number. Thus, the number $X = 2\cdot3\cdot5\cdots p_n + 1$ is surely a natural number greater than 1 and must be divisible by a prime number. But no member of P divides X, and we assumed that all the prime numbers were elements of P. Therefore, our assumption is false and P is infinite. Finally, $P \subset N$ and so, being infinite, is denumerable by Theorem 4.3.

Consider the set of *algebraic numbers*, i.e., solutions of polynomial equations with integral coefficients. An example of such an equation is $6x^7 - 4x^3 + 2x - 18 = 0$. The general form of such equations is

$$a_n x^n + a_{n-1} x^{n-1} + \ldots + a_2 x^2 + a_1 x + a_0 = 0$$

where n is a natural number, a_i is an integer for each $i = 1, 2, \ldots, n$, and $a_n \neq 0$. We show that the set of solutions of all such equations, the set of algebraic numbers, is denumerable in the following way, omitting some of the details. First, let us call the natural number $n + |a_n| + |a_{n-1}| + \ldots + |a_0|$ the *radix* of the polynomial. Clearly, for a given radix we can specify the quantities $n, a_n, a_{n-1}, \ldots, a_0$ in only a finite number of ways thereby obtaining only a finite number of equations. But each such equation has only a finite number of roots so that the set of roots for a given radix (with repetitions deleted) is a finite set. The union of such sets over all radix numbers is countable and certainly infinite, hence denumerable. Observe that the set of rational numbers is a proper subset of the set of algebraic numbers and yet both are denumerable.

. . . .

EXERCISES

1. Prove that $\sim$ defined below is an equivalence relation (m, n, p, q are integers, $n > 0, q > 0$):

$$\frac{m}{n} \sim \frac{p}{q} \Leftrightarrow mq = np$$

2. Prove that $N \sim N' = \{\frac{1}{1}, \frac{2}{1}, \frac{3}{1}, \ldots\}$.

4.6 NON-DENUMERABLE SETS

Having discovered that so many infinite sets are denumerable, the possibility arises that all infinite sets are denumerable. If so, then all sets are either finite or denumerable and there is no point in introducing the word denumerable since we might in that case just say infinite. (This is essentially what the early Greeks did say.) Moreover, if such were the case, the theory of sets probably would have constituted a mere article in a journal in the 1900's and be obscure now. There is some feeling that Cantor's original study was intended to show that all infinite sets are indeed denumerable. Certainly he delayed any publication for some time after beginning the study. But whatever his original plan was, early in his studies Cantor discovered the remarkable fact that not all infinite sets are denumerable.

Perhaps the simplest set with which to illustrate this fact is the set $U = \{x; x \in E_1, 0 < x < 1\}$. We ask the reader to recall that every member of U has a unique decimal expansion of the form $0.b_1b_2b_3 \ldots$ where $b_n \in \{0, 1, \ldots, 9\}$ $\forall$ n. Thus, for example, $\frac{1}{3} = 0.333 \ldots$, $\pi/4 = 0.78539 \ldots$. For those numbers with a terminating decimal such as $\frac{1}{2} = 0.5$, we agree (in order to have uniqueness) to decrease the last digit by one and append 9's so that it will have an infinite expansion. Thus, $\frac{1}{2} = 0.4999 \ldots$ and not $\frac{1}{2} = 0.500 \ldots$. With this point in mind we can say that two members of U are equal if and only if the digits in their respective decimal expansions are identical. Hence, if two such numbers have a *single* decimal place in which the digits are different, they are unequal. This is a very important point on which the ensuing discussion depends quite critically.

Now suppose that the set U is denumerable. Then there is a function f such that $f: N \xrightarrow[1-1]{\text{onto}} U$. We may then pair each element of U with a unique element of N as follows:

$$f(1) = 0.a_{11}a_{12}a_{13} \ldots$$
$$f(2) = 0.a_{21}a_{22}a_{23} \ldots$$
$$f(3) = 0.a_{31}a_{32}a_{33} \ldots$$
$$\vdots$$
$$f(n) = 0.a_{n1}a_{n2}a_{n3} \ldots$$
$$\vdots$$

where $a_{nm} \in \{0,1,2, \ldots ,9\}$ for each $n \in N$ and $m \in N$. Note that the first subscript in a_{nm} denotes the unique integer in N to which the number corresponds, whereas the second subscript denotes the decimal place location of the digit a_{nm}. Note also that our correspondence in no way implies that $f(1) < f(2) < f(3) < \ldots$, i.e., the elements of U are not to be thought of as ordered according to size.

We now construct a number which must belong to U and yet cannot be found as the image of any integer under f. The number is $x = 0.b_1 b_2 b_3 \ldots$ where $b_n = \begin{cases} 1 \text{ if } a_{nn} \neq 1 \\ 2 \text{ if } a_{nn} = 1 \end{cases}$ for each $n \in N$. For example, if our first three members of U happen to be $f(1) = 0.31142 \ldots$, $f(2) = 0.1111 \ldots$, $f(3) = 0.18923 \ldots$, then the first three digits in our number x become $0.121 \ldots$. This is an example of a recursive definition. It must be confessed that the concept is usually a little confusing to the beginner and is perhaps a non-trivial notion in mathematics, justifying the confusion. But, the principle of mathematical induction guarantees that our number x above is perfectly well-defined.

Now $x \neq f(1)$ since $b_1 \neq a_{11}$, $x \neq f(2)$ since $b_2 \neq a_{22}$, and, in general, $x \neq f(n)$ because $b_n \neq a_{nn}$. Since this is true for every $n \in N$, x is not the image of any natural number under f. But x surely belongs to U, which contradicts the fact that f is onto. Having arrived at this contradiction, we can only conclude that our assumption was wrong and that U is non-denumerable! But trivially, U is infinite, for it contains all of the rational numbers between zero and one and that set is denumerable, hence infinite. Thus, we have found a non-denumerable infinite set, and so we see, as Cantor might have, that there is a possibility of classifying infinite sets into various types. Some theorems of a somewhat general nature will be very helpful in making such a classification.

. . . .

THEOREM 4.9

Every infinite set has a denumerable subset.

PROOF

Let A be an infinite set. Then, by definition, there is a set B such that $B \subset A$ and $A \sim B$. Let f be a 1–1 function mapping A onto B. Let $C = A - B$. Since $B \subset A$, $C \neq \varnothing$ and $C \subset A$. Since $C \neq \varnothing$, there exists $x \in C$. We set $x = a_1$ for the sake of definiteness. Now $f(a_1) \in B$ and we set $a_2 = f(a_1)$ and, similarly, $a_3 = f(a_2)$. Having so defined a_k we let $a_{k+1} = f(a_k)$ so that, by induction, a_n is defined for all $n \in N$, and $a_n \in B$ for all $n > 1$ whereas $a_1 \notin B$.

So far our definition does not dismiss the possibility that some of the elements a_n are equal. If such is the case, let m be the smallest subscript for which $a_m = a_k$ for some $k < m$. Clearly, $m > 1$ so that $a_m \in B$. Also, $k \neq 1$ since $a_1 \notin B$, so that $k > 1$. Then $a_m = f(a_{m-1})$, $a_k = f(a_{k-1})$ and $a_m = a_k$ implies $a_{m-1} = a_{k-1}$, since f is 1–1, whereas $m - 1 < m$, contrary to the definition of m. Thus, we conclude that the elements $a_1, a_2, a_3, \ldots$ are all distinct. This being the case, let $A' = \{a_1, a_2, a_3, \ldots\}$. By construction, A' is denumerable and clearly $A' \subseteq A$ as asserted.   Q.E.D.

. . . .

Theorem 4.9 now enables us to establish some results about infinite sets in general that bear a resemblance to properties of denumerable sets previously established.

. . . .

THEOREM 4.10

Let A be any infinite set. If $B \subseteq A$, B is countable and $A - B$ is infinite, then $A \sim A - B$.

PROOF

Let $C = A - B$. Then C is infinite by hypothesis and hence has a denumerable subset C' by Theorem 4.9. Let $D = C - C'$ (D may be empty). Then we have $C = C' \cup D$ where $C' \cap D = \varnothing$ (as the reader may easily verify). Moreover, B is finite or denumerable, C' is denumerable, so that $B \cup C'$ is denumerable by Theorem 4.5 or 4.6 (whichever applies). Since $B \cup C'$ and C' are both denumerable, $B \cup C' \sim C'$ and we let $f \colon B \cup C' \xrightarrow[1-1]{\text{onto}} C'$. Finally, $A = B \cup C = B \cup (C' \cup D)$ $= (B \cup C') \cup D$ with $(B \cup C') \cap D = \varnothing$. (That $B \cap D = \varnothing$ follows from the fact that $D \subset C$ and $B \cap C = \varnothing$.) We now construct a mapping from A to C which will establish the necessary 1–1 correspondence.

Define

$$\varphi(a) = \begin{cases} a & \text{if } a \in D \\ f(a) & \text{if } a \in B \cup C' \end{cases}$$

for each $a \in A$. Clearly, $\varphi \colon A \longrightarrow C$ and we will supply the details to prove that φ is 1–1 and onto.

Suppose $a_1, a_2 \in A$ and $a_1 \neq a_2$. Now three distinct cases arise which we can dispose of as follows. If $a_1, a_2 \in D$, then $\varphi(a_1) = a_1 \neq a_2 = \varphi(a_2)$. If $a_1, a_2 \in B \cup C'$, then $\varphi(a_1) = f(a_1) \neq f(a_2) = \varphi(a_2)$ since f is 1–1. Finally, if $a_1 \in D$ and $a_2 \in B \cup C'$, then $f(a_2) \in C'$ so that $a_1 \neq f(a_2)$ since $D \cap C' = \varnothing$. Thus, $\varphi(a_1) = a_1 \neq f(a_2) = \varphi(a_2)$, and so φ is 1–1.

Suppose $y \in C$. Then $y \in C'$ or $y \in D$. If $y \in C'$, then there is an $x \in B \cup C'$ (hence $x \in A$) such that $f(x) = y$ (since f is onto) and $\varphi(x) = f(x) = y$. If $y \in D$, then let $x = y$ so that $\varphi(x) = y$ with $x \in A$. Hence, in both cases there is an $x \in A$ such that $\varphi(x) = y$ and φ is onto.

Having shown that φ is 1–1 and onto, we have $A \sim C$, i.e., $A \sim A - B$ as asserted. Q.E.D.

. . . .

THEOREM 4.11

If A is any infinite set and B any countable set, then $A \sim A \cup B$.

PROOF

Let $D = B - A$ (D may be empty) and $C = A \cup D$. Now $D \subseteq B$ so that D is finite or denumerable. Also, C is infinite since $A \subseteq C$ and A is infinite. Hence, $A = C - D \sim C$ by Theorem 4.10, since A is infinite. But $C = A \cup B$ also so that $A \sim A \cup B$ as asserted. Q.E.D.

. . . .

Intuitively, Theorem 4.10 says that if we begin with an infinite set and take out a finite or denumerable set of points, the remaining set is still equivalent to the first, provided only that it is infinite. This will have special significance in the next chapter. Theorem 4.11 says that if we adjoin a finite or denumerable set of points to an infinite set, the resulting set is still equivalent to the former.

As an application of Theorem 4.10, consider the set $U = \{x;$ $x \in E_1, 0 < x < 1\}$ which was defined earlier. Let B be the set of rational numbers in U. Then $B \subset U$, and we have already seen that B is denumerable. Also, $U - B$, the set of irrational numbers in U, is infinite $(1/(n\sqrt{2})$ is irrational and in U for every n, hence infinitely many n) so that by the theorem $U - B \sim U$. Thus, the set of irrationals in U is equivalent to U itself!

To see some of the implications of Theorem 4.11, consider U again. In accordance with analysis, let us denote by $[a,b]$ (where $a < b$ are any two real numbers) the set of real numbers between a and b inclusive, which we call a *closed interval*. More specifically, $[a,b] = \{x; x \in E_1, a \leq x \leq b\}$. Now, in particular, $[0,1] = U \cup \{0\} \cup \{1\}$ and, by Theorem 4.11, $[0,1] \sim U$. Next, let a and b be any two real numbers with $a < b$. Let $f(x) = (b - a)x + a \ \forall$ $x \in [0,1]$. Then f maps $[0,1]$ onto $[a,b]$ and is certainly 1–1.

Since a and b were arbitrarily chosen, we have the important result that any two closed intervals, no matter what their lengths, are equivalent to $[0,1]$, hence to each other. Thus, e.g., $[-(1/2^{10}),$ $1/2^{10}] \sim [-(2^{10}), 2^{10}]$ in spite of the fact that the length of the former, $1/2^9$, is much smaller than the length of the latter, 2^{11}. Of course we may, in accordance with Theorem 4.10, delete either the point a or b (or both) from $[a,b]$ and the resulting set is still equivalent to $[a,b]$.

Even more is true. As before, let E_1 denote the entire set of real numbers. The 1–1 function $f(x) = \tan x$ for $-\pi/2 < x < \pi/2$ maps the set $\{x; x \in E_1, -\pi/2 < x < \pi/2\}$ onto E_1. Consequently, $[0,1] \sim E_1$ and $[a,b] \sim E_1$ for any closed interval! Let I denote the set of irrational numbers and R the set of rational numbers. R is denumerable, $I = E_1 - R$ and is infinite so that $I \sim E_1$ by Theorem 4.10. Let T denote the set of real transcendental numbers, i.e., real numbers that are not algebraic. Letting A denote the set of real algebraic numbers, $T = E_1 - A$, T is infinite, A denumerable so again $T \sim E_1$.

Finally, let $S = \{(x,y); x \in U, y \in U\}$. Geometrically, S is the set of points in the plane interior to the unit square. Then if $(x, y) \in S$, $x = 0.a_1a_2 \ldots$, $y = 0.b_1b_2 \ldots$ and we define $f((x, y)) = z$ where $z = 0.a_1b_1a_2b_2 \ldots$. Then f is 1–1 and maps S onto $(0, 1)$ so that $S \sim U$. Since $E_2 = \{(x,y); x \in E_1, y \in E_1\}$, it can be shown, as above, that $E_2 \sim S$ so that $E_2 \sim E_1$. More generally, $E_n = \{(x_1,x_2, \ldots ,x_n); x_k \in E_1, k = 1,2, \ldots ,n\} \sim E_1$ for every natural number n. Thus, as sets of points under equivalence, dimension in Euclidean spaces loses its significance.

With the results just established we see that in classifying sets it is not a matter of only finite and infinite sets as was thought for many centuries. So far we have divided infinite sets into denumerable and non-denumerable. Even so, is it the case that all non-denumerable sets are equivalent to E_1? The answer is negative as we will show in the next chapter, and in fact infinite sets may be classified into various levels of "infinity," there being no ultimate level.

. . . .

EXERCISES

1. Let A be a set. Show that $A \times \{0\} \sim A$.

2. Let A and B be sets. Show that $A \times B \sim B \times A$.

3. If A, B, and C are sets, show that $A \times (B \times C) \sim (A \times B) \times C$.

4. Let $A \neq \emptyset$ be finite and B be denumerable. Show that $A \times B$ is denumerable.

5. If A, B, C, and D are sets, $A \sim B$, and $C \sim D$, show that $A \times C \sim B \times D$.

5

CARDINAL NUMBERS

5.1 GENERAL REMARKS

At the close of the last chapter it was suggested that sets might be classified into finer classifications than merely finite and infinite. The task of the present chapter is to carry out a program of classification that will not only characterize infinite sets, but finite sets as well. Indeed, the latter will serve as a guide to effect the former.

The first problem in classification is the selection of some criterion which may be used to distinguish various sets. One that naturally suggests itself is size, but we will have to decide what we mean by size. With finite sets the task seems easy enough—just let size mean the number of elements in the set. After all, we can count them (although even this is tedious when the number of elements is quite large). But what of the number of elements in an infinite set? About all our intuition tells us is that there are infinitely many elements in such a set, and this defeats our purpose of trying to distinguish between sets. Hence, we will have to make some suitable definition of "number of elements" of a set in such a way that the definition will be compatible with our intuitive knowledge of finite sets and, at the same time, extend to infinite sets. In this way, the concept of number will be generalized. This was another one of Cantor's great achievements, and not only did he provide such a generalized concept, but he also went on to establish an arithmetic for these new objects. These are the matters we wish to present at this time.

In establishing the results of this chapter, there is an over-all plan of attack that will be followed and it might be well to bring it to the attention of the reader. We will first investigate a certain property of finite sets and then generalize this notion to arbitrary sets by a suitable definition. Having made the general definition we will investigate some of the consequences and hope to effect our classification in so doing.

5.2 DEFINITION OF CARDINAL NUMBER OF A SET

First, let us consider the simplest of finite sets, namely, one of the sets $N_k = \{1, 2, \ldots, k\}$. Whatever we adopt for a definition of the number of elements of a set, we would certainly want to say that N_k has exactly k elements. Moreover, if A is any finite set, we know that $A \sim N_k$ for some k. Consequently, we are tempted to say, on the basis of the 1–1 correspondence between A and N_k, that A too has exactly k elements. Finally, if B is another finite set and $B \sim A$, we should say B has exactly k elements because it follows that $B \sim N_k$ also. Then we would say that A and B have the same number of elements simply because they are equivalent sets and, moreover, that number is k.

Thus, the concept of the number of elements of a set seems to be closely associated with the notion of equivalence. Let us call the number of elements of N_k *the cardinal number of N_k* and denote it $\#(N_k)$. Thus, $\#(N_k) = k$. To every finite set A such that $A \sim N_k$ we define, similarly, $\#(A) = k$. It then follows that if $A \sim B$, $\#(A) = \#(B)$, and the problem is pretty well settled for finite sets with the further agreement that $\#(\varnothing) = 0$, which seems very natural.

Observe that for the finite set A just discussed, apart from the fact that $\#(A) = k$, $\#(A)$ is really a property which is shared by all sets equivalent to A. Indeed, Cantor defined the cardinal number of a set A to be the set of all sets equivalent to A, and he denoted this by $\overline{\overline{A}}$. Thus, $\overline{\overline{A}} = \{B; B \text{ is a set}, B \sim A\}$. If we let k serve the double duty of denoting the natural number k as well as the cardinal number of A, then $k = \overline{\overline{A}}$. For example, $2 = \{B; B \text{ is a set}, B \sim \{1,2\}\}$. It then appears awkward to write, e.g., $\{a,b\} \in 2$, but only because of the use of the symbol 2 in the sense of cardinal number. This is another approach to the notion of cardinal number, and it has a lot of intuitive appeal. We think, however, that the line of thought we are following has as much appeal, although possibly no approach would be completely satisfactory.

To continue our pursuit, what shall we say about the cardinal number of an infinite set? Consider, for example, the denumerable sets. In the finite case we were able to find a sort of standard set, namely, N_k, against which, by means of equivalence, we could compare other finite sets to determine whether or not they had k elements. We define $\#(N_k) = k$ simply because k is intuitively the number of elements in N_k. This might suggest the approach to be used for denumerable sets. In fact, the set N of all natural numbers served to define denumerability, hence why not use N as a norming set or standard to define cardinal number for denumerable sets?

This line of reasoning is all right as far as it goes. We could say that all denumerable sets have the same cardinal number as N because they are all equivalent to N. This would be consistent with our notion, expressed above, that the cardinal number of a set is simply a property common to all equivalent sets. But what is the cardinal number of N? It is hopeless to suggest that N has "so many" elements because no number in our experience can be used to replace the phrase "so many." We could say N has as many elements as any set equivalent to N but then we are back where we started. The trouble lies in the fact that we are trying to define the notion of the number of elements of N in terms of the number of elements of N. (For finite sets this was no problem since the number of elements in N_k is quite clear to us. But at the same time it must be confessed that if we were to stop with finite sets, it would hardly have been worth the trouble to develop cardinal numbers, since, with each finite set, we immediately associate a natural number k, and the properties and arithmetic of the latter set of objects are well known.)

What is needed for infinite sets, then, is a new object to be called the cardinal number of the set and taken to measure the number of elements of that set. In view of the preceding remarks, we then make the following definition.

. . . .

DEFINITION 5.1

Let A be an infinite set. *The cardinal number of A*, denoted $\#(A)$, is a primitive object with the property that $\#(A) = \#(B) \Leftrightarrow A \sim B$.*

. . . .

You may feel a little uneasy about Definition 5.1 because we do not say what a cardinal number is, but only that it possesses a certain property. But our objective was, in fact, to introduce a new primitive for lack of existing objects that would serve the avowed purpose. Moreover, by this point, you should be somewhat willing to accept the admission of primitive notions in mathematical systems. After all, you studied geometry which consisted of a body of statements about points when point was never really defined. Indeed, we have spent all this space discussing sets without having

---

* Strictly speaking, this is an axiom since a new primitive is introduced.

defined set.   In other words, we do not say what a set is but rather when sets are equal and when objects belong to sets, etc.   Yet, we hope that by this time you are quite willing to accept the notion of set and admit certain objects as sets without too much uneasiness, in spite of the fact that set was undefined.   Just as, having studied geometry, one accepts the fact that a line segment from A to B is a well-defined collection of points with point left undefined, so too, one learns to accept and work with primitives such as cardinal numbers.

At this point we have cardinal numbers for all finite sets and indeed have identified these with each of the non-negative integers.   In addition, Definition 5.1 furnishes us with at least two more distinct cardinal numbers, namely $\#(N)$ and $\#(E_1)$.   That they are distinct follows from the fact that N is not equivalent to E_1.   For purposes of distinguishing between cardinal numbers for finite sets and infinite sets, we will occasionally refer to the former as *finite* cardinal numbers and the latter as *transfinite* cardinal numbers.

5.3   ORDERING CARDINAL NUMBERS

We now have a means of telling when two cardinal numbers are equal and when they are unequal.   In the latter case, however, we are not satisfied with saying two cardinal numbers are unequal.   We would like to be able to say, in addition, when one is less than the other.   Why should we want more than equality?   Looking back we see that, in defining equality of cardinal numbers, we were attempting to put meaning into the statement "sets A and B have the same number of elements."   The meaning is established by writing $\#(A) = \#(B)$.   Then it is natural to inquire further into the question, "Given two sets which do not have the same number of elements (in the above sense), which of the two has fewer elements?"

The answer to our question would appear to lie in the framework of ordering cardinal numbers. Since there is no natural meaning for the symbol $\#(A) < \#(B)$ when both are transfinite cardinals, we shall have to define what we mean by $<$ in this case. Now we do know what is meant by $m < n$ for finite cardinal numbers m and n because these are natural numbers. At least we know what is meant by the symbol $m < n$ in the sense that there is already a natural ordering defined for natural numbers. Whether or not that same ordering will serve to define what we mean by "fewer elements than" remains to be seen. As before, we rely on our finite sets and our intuitive knowledge of these sets to make a general definition.

When m and n are finite cardinal numbers, what meaning for the sets they represent does the statement $m < n$ have, where $m < n$ means the usual ordering of the natural numbers? Well, $m = \#(N_m)$ and $n = \#(N_n)$. Since $N_m = \{1,2,3,\ldots,m\}$ and $N_n = \{1,2,3,\ldots,n\}$, we see that $N_m \subset N_n$. Thus, it would appear, the relation for the corresponding sets is that of $\subset$. Certainly, N_m has fewer elements than N_n—all our intuition tells us so— and this is what we were looking for. Accordingly, it would appear that we should define $\#(A) < \#(B)$ if $A \subset B$ for any two sets A and B. We would then say A has fewer elements than B. A little investigation would reveal, however, that the choice was poor. In the first place, regarding the set N of natural numbers and the set E of even natural numbers, we would say E has fewer elements than N (and most readers would resound in agreement although by this time we hope you are a little more cautious in relying on intuition). At the same time, we are forced to say E and N have the same number of elements because $E \sim N$. Our definition would be poor indeed.

Perhaps the reader has often heard a phrase like, "Oh well, in mathematics we are free to define things as we please." This is partly true and partly false. It is true in the sense that we do have a great deal of freedom to define at will provided we are willing to accept the consequences. But there are many times when the consequences of some tentative definition are too dire to admit, and we discard it immediately.   A case in point is the preceding definition.

Even if it were not for the fact that infinite sets are equivalent to (hence have as many elements as) a proper subset, we would not care to adopt the above definition for finite sets.   Thus, if A and B are finite sets with $A \cap B = \varnothing$, it is not always the case that either $A \subset B$ or $B \subset A$, and we would not be able to compare A and B at all with respect to the ordering of their cardinal numbers.   Certainly one of the properties of "less than" that we would like very much to have is that if A and B are arbitrary sets they are comparable, i.e., exactly one of the statements $\#(A) < \#(B)$ or $\#(B) = \#(A)$ or $\#(B) < \#(A)$ is true.   Hence, we shall have to look further into the meaning of $m < n$ for the corresponding sets.

Let A and B be finite sets.   Further, suppose $m = \#(A)$ and $n = \#(B)$, where $m < n$, so that $A \sim N_m$ and $B \sim N_n$.   Accordingly, we write $A = \{a_1, a_2, \dots, a_m\}$ and $B = \{b_1, b_2, \dots, b_n\}$. Now $N_m \subset N_n$ and, if we let $B_m = \{b_1, b_2, \dots, b_m\}$, we have $B_m \subset B$.   Then the mapping $\varphi(a_k) = b_k$, $k = 1, 2, \dots, m$ is 1–1 and maps A onto B_m.   Of course, it is not possible to map B onto a subset of A because if A_1 is any subset of A then $A_1 \sim N_k$ for some k and clearly $k \leq m$.   If $B \sim A_1$ then $n = k \leq m$ contrary to our assumption $m < n$.   Since A and B are arbitrary finite sets, this procedure suggests our general definition.

. . . .

DEFINITION 5.2

Let A and B be sets.   Then $\#(A)$ *is less than* $\#(B)$, denoted $\#(A) < \#(B)$, if A is equivalent to a subset of B but B is equivalent to no subset of A.

. . . .

Having made our definition, we see that it agrees with what we think ought to be the case when A and B are finite sets.   In addition, we avoid the situation described above regarding the infinite sets E and N.   Thus, E is equivalent to a subset of N, namely, E itself (under the identity map), but N is equivalent to a subset of

E, namely, E itself (under the mapping $f(n) = 2n$), so that it is not true that E has fewer elements than N in spite of its being a proper subset of N.

Rather than turn at this point to specific examples and consequences of our definition, it would be well to see first whether or not the definition was worth the effort. By this we mean that unless we have some transfinite cardinal numbers besides $\#(N)$ and $\#(E_1)$ we might as well settle the ordering for $\#(N)$ and $\#(E_1)$ (which is an easy matter, as we shall see) and stop there. So our next task will be to show the existence of more cardinal numbers, and we will find that there are an unlimited number of distinct transfinite cardinal numbers.

. . . .

THEOREM 5.1

Let A be any set and $p(A)$ the power set of A. Then $\#(A) < \#(p(A))$.

PROOF

First, if $A = \varnothing$, then $0 = \#(\varnothing)$, $1 = \#(p(\varnothing))$, and $0 < 1$. If $A \neq \varnothing$, then $\forall$ $a \in A$ we have $\{a\} \subseteq A$ hence $\{a\} \in p(A)$. By means of the mapping $\varphi(a) = \{a\}$, A is mapped into $p(A)$ and, letting $B = \{\{a\} ; a \in A\}$ we have $B \subset p(A)$ and φ maps A onto B. Clearly φ is 1–1 so that $A \sim B$ under φ.

Suppose $A_1 \subseteq A$ and $A_1 \sim p(A)$ under the mapping f, say. Let $C_a = f(a)$ be the image in $p(A)$ of each $a \in A_1$. Let $D = \{a; a \in A_1, a \notin C_a\}$. Since $D \subseteq A$ we must have $D \in p(A)$. But then since f maps A_1 onto $p(A)$, there must exist $a_1 \in A_1$ such that $f(a_1) = D$. Then we may also write $D = C_{a_1}$ according to our notation above. Now either $a_1 \in D$ or $a_1 \notin D$. But if $a_1 \in D$ then $a_1 \notin C_{a_1}$ by definition of D while $C_{a_1} = D$ so both $a_1 \in D$ and $a_1 \notin D$, which is absurd. On the other hand, if $a_1 \notin D$, since $D = C_{a_1}$, $a_1 \notin C_{a_1}$ so we should have $a_1 \in D$ and we arrive at the same absurdity. Hence, our assumption must be false and we conclude that $p(A)$ is equivalent to no subset of A.

By definition 5.2, $\#(A) < \#(p(A))$. Q.E.D.

. . . .

The results of Theorem 5.1 are far-reaching. We now know that there are cardinal numbers larger than $\#(E_1)$. Thus, we might write $\#(E_1) < \#(p(E_1)) < \#(p(p(E_1))) < \#(p(p(p(E_1)))) < \ldots$. Moreover, there is no largest cardinal number. For if we assume contrariwise that the set M exists such that $\#(M)$ is the largest cardinal number, then $\#(M) < \#(p(M))$ by the theorem and we find a set $p(M)$ with a larger cardinal number. We thus see that our definition of $<$ has a great deal of content. To partially complete our task we need two more results.

Before proceeding, however, we adopt some conventions that are typical. First, we agree that $\#(A) > \#(B)$, where $>$ is read "greater than," is just another way of writing $\#(B) < \#(A)$. Secondly, let $\#(A) \leq \#(B)$ mean $\#(A) < \#(B)$ or $\#(A) = \#(B)$. Finally, it is sometimes useful to adopt a symbol for the special cardinal numbers $\#(N)$ and $\#(E_1)$. There is some agreement on $\#(E_1)$. We denote it by c for "continuum" and say E_1 has cardinal *continuum* (as does every set equivalent to E_1, of course). Unfortunately, the same thing cannot be said about $\#(N)$. Originally, Cantor used $\aleph_0$ (read aleph-null) where $\aleph$ is the first letter of the Hebrew alphabet. Since there is no general agreement we will use α, not having used it in any special context, and henceforth $\alpha = \#(N)$. We will use the Greek letters μ, ν, ρ, etc., to denote the cardinal number of an arbitrary set and, of course, we accordingly assume that ν, for example, is a cardinal number (or, more briefly, cardinal) if and only if there exists a set A such that $\nu = \#(A)$. With the above agreements in mind we now establish an important result.

. . . .

THEOREM 5.2

If k is any finite cardinal, then $k < \alpha$. If β is any transfinite cardinal, $\alpha \leq \beta$.

PROOF

We know that $k = \#(N_k)$ and $\alpha = \#(N)$. But $N_k \subset N \; \forall \; k$, hence $N_k \sim N_k \subset N$. On the other hand, N is not equivalent to any subset of

N_k because by Theorem 4.2 this would make N finite. Thus, the first result is established.

Let B be an infinite set with $\beta = \#(B)$. If B is denumerable, then $\beta = \alpha$ and there is nothing to prove. Suppose B is non-denumerable. By Theorem 4.9, B has a denumerable subset A. Then $N \sim A \subset B$. If B is equivalent to some subset N' of N then, since N' is either finite or denumerable by Theorem 4.3 and since we are given B is infinite, B must be denumerable contrary to our supposition. Thus, if B is non-denumerable, B is not equivalent to any subset of N. By Definition 5.2, $\alpha < \beta$ in this case. Hence, in all cases, $\alpha \leq \beta$ as asserted.   Q.E.D.

. . . .

We see by Theorem 5.2 that α is the smallest transfinite cardinal number. Also, since E_1 is non-denumerable we see by the proof that $\alpha < c$. Hence, we may now order the special cardinal numbers dealt with so far as $0 < 1 < 2 \ldots < n < n + 1 < \ldots < \alpha < c < \ldots$. Regarding the inequality $\alpha < c$, we might ask whether or not there is some cardinal number ν with the property that $\alpha < \nu < c$. To relate it more to sets, do there exist non-denumerable infinite subsets of E_1 with cardinal number less than the continuum? Cantor was convinced that the answer was no and, it is said,[*] his desperate attempts to prove it provoked a breakdown in his health. Nevertheless, we do not have an answer to this day. No one has been able to show that such a set exists nor prove that such a set cannot exist. In spite of this, we lean toward Cantor and hypothesize that the answer to our question is no. This hypothesis has come to be known as the *Continuum Hypothesis*.

More generally, the *Generalized Continuum Hypothesis* is the hypothesis that for any *infinite* set A there is no cardinal number between $\#(A)$ and $\#(p(A))$. Of course this is not true of finite sets. Thus, $2 = \#(\{0,1\})$ whereas $4 = \#(p(\{0,1\})) = \#(\{\varnothing, \{0\}, \{1\}, \{0,1\}\})$ and $2 < 3 < 4$. Thus, if we were to use finite sets as our guide we would suspect the Continuum Hypothesis of being false. The brilliant mathematician Gödel has proved that at least the

---

[*] Abraham A. Fraenkel, *Abstract Set Theory* (Amsterdam: North-Holland Publishing Company, 1961), p. 69.

assumption of the Generalized Continuum Hypothesis (which we will see in Section 5.5 includes the Continuum Hypothesis as a special case) as an added axiom in set theory produces no contradiction.*

We mentioned above that if we adopted $\subset$ to define $<$ for cardinal numbers, we would soon discover that two sets may be incomparable in the sense that we could not compare their cardinal numbers with respect to $<$. The same question should of course be asked about the present definition of $<$. In other words, if $\#(A) \neq \#(B)$, can we say that either $\#(A) > \#(B)$ or $\#(A) < \#(B)$? The answer to the question turns out to be yes. But the proof is not a trivial one at all, and we shall not attempt to give one but ask that the reader accept the following theorem without proof for the time being.

. . . .

THEOREM 5.3

(Trichotomy Law.) Let A and B be sets. Then exactly one of the following statements is true:

(i) $\#(A) = \#(B)$

(ii) $\#(A) < \#(B)$

(iii) $\#(A) > \#(B)$

PROOF

Not given.

. . . .

We close this section with another very important theorem but again one whose proof is considered beyond the level of the course. This theorem is known as the equivalence theorem, and it offers yet another way of establishing equality of cardinal numbers through the ordering of cardinal numbers. We will actually give a proof of the theorem by assuming a certain lemma without proof. How-

---

* Patrick Suppes, *Axiomatic Set Theory* (Princeton, N. J.: D. Van Nostrand Company, Inc., 1960), p. 194.

ever, we want to caution the reader that the lemma we assume is equivalent to the theorem itself so that, in a sense, we have no proof at all. This is important for we do not want to give the impression that the equivalence theorem is a trivial matter, and the proof of the lemma involves, in fact, all the inherent difficulties of the proof of the theorem itself. But we think the reader will find the lemma quite plausible and intuitively appealing.

. . . .

LEMMA 5.1

Let A and B be sets. If $A \subset B$ then $\#(A) \leq \#(B)$.

PROOF

Not given.

. . . .

Notice that the lemma is trivially true if A and B are finite although this is not always an infallible guide. An appealing argument for proving the lemma is the following. If $\#(A) > \#(B)$, then by definition B is equivalent to a subset of A but A is not equivalent to a subset of B. But $A \sim A$ under the identity map and $A \subseteq B$, which is a contradiction. By the trichotomy law we conclude $\#(A) \leq \#(B)$. The trouble here is we have quoted Theorem 5.3 for which a proof was not given. Moreover, though we did not indicate it at the time, that theorem does not seem to admit a proof with the meager equipment generated so far. That being the case, it should not be used at this point to validate the above argument. It is very easy to fall into this and similar traps regarding the equivalence theorem. Again, we point out that a proof of the lemma can be given which does not depend on Theorem 5.3, and we prove the theorem on that assumption.*

---

* The proof reduces to the following assertion. If $A_1 \subseteq A$, $A \subseteq B$, and $B \sim A_1$, then $B \sim A$. Then, with $A \subseteq B$, we may say either $A \sim B$ or, if not, B is not equivalent to any subset of A, for otherwise it would stand in contradiction to the assertion just made. This is another statement equivalent to the theorem itself.

. . . .

THEOREM 5.4

(Equivalence Theorem.)   Let A and B be sets.   If A is equivalent to a subset of B and B is equivalent to a subset of A, then $\#(A) = \#(B)$, i.e., $A \sim B$.

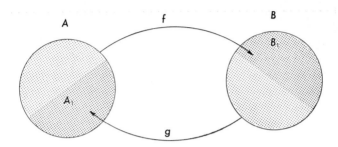

FIGURE 5.1 • The maps f and g

PROOF

By hypothesis there is a set B_1 such that $B_1 \subseteq B$ and $A \sim B_1$ under, say, f.   Similarly, there is a set A_1 such that $A_1 \subseteq A$ and $B \sim A_1$ under g, say (cf. Figure 5.1).   Let us set $C = B - B_1$ (C may be empty—we have only pictured it as non-empty) so that $B = B_1 \cup C$ with $B_1 \sim A$.

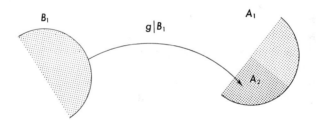

FIGURE 5.2 • The mapping $g \mid B_1$

Similarly, let $A_2 = g(B_1)$ so that $g \mid B_1$ establishes $A_2 \sim B_1$ (cf. Figure 5.2) and, letting $D = A_1 - A_2$ (D may be empty), $A_1 = A_2 \cup D$ with $A_2 \sim B_1$.   Then $A_2 \sim A$ since $B_1 \sim A$.

Now, from $A_2 \subseteq A_1$, $\#(A_2) \leq \#(A_1)$ by Lemma 5.1. Also, from $A_1 \subseteq A$, $\#(A_1) \leq \#(A)$ by the same lemma. If $\#(A_1) < \#(A)$, then (see Exercise 5.3–1) we would have $\#(A_2) < \#(A)$ contradicting the fact that $A_2 \sim A$. Hence, we conclude that $\#(A_1) = \#(A)$ or $A_1 \sim A$. Then, since $B \sim A_1$, we have $A \sim B$ or $\#(A) = \#(B)$ as asserted.   Q.E.D.

· ·

The Equivalence Theorem was first conjectured by Cantor himself although he did not supply a proof. Later, the two mathematicians Schroeder and Bernstein gave independent proofs, and the theorem is accordingly often called the Schroeder-Bernstein theorem. For a proof of our lemma and/or the theorem, the reader may consult some of the sources given in the bibliography.

· ·

EXERCISES

1. If $\#(A) \leq \#(B)$ and $\#(B) < \#(C)$, prove that $\#(A) < \#(C)$.
2. If $A \sim B_1$ and $B_1 \subseteq B$ prove that $\#(A) \leq \#(B)$.
3. Prove that Lemma 5.1 holds if A and B are countable.

5.4 ADDITION AND MULTIPLICATION OF CARDINAL NUMBERS

We would now like to establish an arithmetic for cardinal numbers by means of which we can add and multiply these new objects. Of course, we already have an arithmetic for finite cardinals as well as certain other well-known properties. Hence, we would not want to define addition and multiplication in general in any way that would change these already existing properties. In other words, whatever our definitions are, we want them to conform to known properties in the special case when the cardinals are finite. Secondly, we would hope that certain finite properties, such as commutativity for example, will also hold for the transfinite cardinals. The reader may have already guessed that the prospect of preserving all familiar properties is doomed to failure because of some of the peculiarities of transfinite cardinals. Even so, we will see that a surprising number of them are preserved.

As usual, we turn first to finite sets to decide what our definitions should be. What do we mean by the addition of 2 and 3 when the latter are regarded as cardinal numbers of sets? We know that $2 + 3 = 5$, and if we examine the set N_5, we see that $N_5 = N_3 \cup \{4,5\}$ so that $5 = \#(N_5)$ and $3 = \#(N_3)$, $2 = \#(\{4,5\})$ so that this suggests taking in general a set with cardinal 3, a set with cardinal 2 and looking at the union to get cardinal 5 as the sum of 2 and 3. But can these sets be arbitrary? Certainly not, for if $A = \{a,b,c\}$ and $B = \{c,d\}$, then $\#(A) = 3, \#(B) = 2$ but $A \cup B = \{a,b,c,d\}$ and $\#(A \cup B) = 4$. We see that what is needed is the extra requirement that A and B be disjoint. This prompts our general definition.

. . . .

DEFINITION 5.3

Let μ and ν be two arbitrary cardinal numbers. The *sum of μ and ν*, denoted $\mu + \nu$, is the cardinal number of $B \cup C$ where B and C are any disjoint sets having cardinals μ and ν respectively. In symbols, let $\mu = \#(B)$ and $\nu = \#(C)$ with $B \cap C = \varnothing$. Then $\mu + \nu = \#(B \cup C)$.

. . . .

A word or two about the definition. First, we only use the phrase "cardinal number" in connection with sets. Thus the phrase "let μ be a cardinal number" has inherent in it the assumption that there is a set B with $\mu = \#(B)$. Hence, given μ and ν we can say there are sets B and C with $\#(B) = \mu$ and $\#(C) = \nu$. But how do we know that we can always find B and C so that $B \cap C = \varnothing$? The next theorem assures us that we can.

· ·

THEOREM 5.5

Let μ and ν be arbitrary cardinal numbers. There exist disjoint sets having μ and ν as cardinal numbers.

PROOF

Let B and C be two sets such that $\mu = \#(B)$ and $\nu = \#(C)$. Let $B' = B \times \{0\}$ and $C' = C \times \{1\}$. Then $B \sim B'$ and $C \sim C'$ by Exercise 4.6–1. Moreover, each member of B' is of the form $(b,0)$ whereas each member of C' is of the form $(c,1)$. All such elements differ in at least the second coordinate so that no elements can be common to B' and C' by the definition of ordered pairs. Thus, $\mu = \#(B')$ and $\nu = \#(C')$ with $B' \cap C' = \varnothing$. Q.E.D.

· ·

The theorem now insures that addition of cardinal numbers is well-defined, and we examine some of the consequences of that definition. Certain well-known properties of the finite cardinal numbers are preserved merely because the corresponding properties hold for sets. The next theorem and Exercises 5.4–1 and 5.4–2 exemplify this fact.

· ·

THEOREM 5.6

Let μ and ν be arbitrary cardinal numbers. Then $\mu + \nu = \nu + \mu$.

PROOF

Let B and C be disjoint sets with $\mu = \#(B), \nu = \#(C)$. Then $\mu + \nu = \#(B \cup C)$. But $E \cup C = C \cup B$ so that $\nu + \mu = \#(C \cup B) = \#(B \cup C) = \mu + \nu$. Q.E.D.

· ·

There are some respects, however, in which the transfinite cardinal addition does not agree with the finite case. Thus, if n is a finite cardinal, $n + 1 > n$. But $\alpha + 1 = \alpha$ according to Theorem 4.5. Indeed, $\alpha + \alpha = \alpha$ using Theorem 4.6, and, in the finite case, this is true of only the cardinal number 0. Also, letting R denote the set of rationals and S the set of irrationals, $E_1 = S \cup R$

with $S \cap R = \varnothing$ showing that $c + \alpha = c$. Exercises 5.4–3 and 5.4–4 illustrate other differences.

In passing, let us observe that in finite cardinal arithmetic, the existence of a unique x such that $n + x = m$ allows us to define $x = m - n$, the difference of two cardinal numbers directly (at least for $m \geq n$). However, we notice here that $\alpha + x = \alpha$ has all sorts of solutions in x, namely, $x = 0, 1, 2, \ldots, \alpha$ so that this in itself is enough to see that any attempt to define subtraction in the transfinite case would be futile.

Our work on set unions shows us that we have no limit on the number of sets whose union can be formed. Suppose C_t is a set for each $t \in T$ where T is an arbitrary index set. Thus, T might be finite, denumerable, or non-denumerable. At any rate, $\bigcup_{t \in T} C_t$ is a well-defined set. This leads us to the notion of generalized cardinal addition whereby we do not restrict ourselves to two sets.

. . . .

DEFINITION 5.4

Let T be an index set and C_t a set for each $t \in T$ such that $\gamma_t = \#(C_t)$ and $C_t \cap C_r = \varnothing$ if $t \neq r$. Then the *sum of the cardinal numbers* γ_t, denoted $\sum_{t \in T} \gamma_t$, is defined by $\sum_{t \in T} \gamma_t = \#(\bigcup_{t \in T} C_t)$.

. . . .

Now, let us turn our attention to the product of cardinal numbers. What set implications are involved in the statement $2 \cdot 3 = 6$ for finite cardinal numbers? Letting $N_2 = \{1,2\}$ and $N_3 = \{1,2,3\}$, a little experimentation might reveal that $N_2 \times N_3 = \{(1,1), (1,2), (1,3), (2,1), (2,2), (2,3)\}$ has cardinal number 6. Further examination would reveal that this is no mere special case and in fact $m \cdot n$ can always be viewed as the cardinal number of $A \times B$ where $m = \#(A)$ and $n = \#(B)$ for finite m and n. Moreover, the sets A and B need not even be disjoint. The reader will want to try several examples. This situation prompts us to define the general product as follows.

· ·

DEFINITION 5.5

Let μ and ν be arbitrary cardinal numbers with sets A and B such that $\mu = \#(A)$, $\nu = \#(B)$. Then the *product of μ and ν*, denoted $\mu \cdot \nu$ (or simply $\mu\nu$) is defined by $\mu\nu = \#(A \times B)$.

· ·

Some consequences of our definition are immediate, and we find that many of the familiar properties of finite cardinal arithmetic are preserved. Exercises 5.4–5 through 5.4–9 will illustrate several of these.

Although similarities to ordinary arithmetic are quite striking in the exercises, it should be observed that there are differences as well. Here, as well as in the material on addition, is a good illustration of the price one often has to pay in generalizing a given concept. In an effort to generalize the concept of number, certain properties of those numbers that we ordinarily consider important no longer hold. It is a matter of weighing the advantages to be gained with the disadvantages. In this case we consider the price worth paying. Let us examine some of these "lost properties."

For finite cardinals the equation $n \cdot x = n$ is satisfied by $x = 1$ only; i.e., 1 is unique in this respect. But for transfinite cardinals this uniqueness is lost. Thus, from Exercise 5.4–8, $\alpha \cdot 1 = \alpha$. However, from Theorem 4.7 we have $\alpha = \#(N \times N) = \alpha \cdot \alpha$. Moreover, by Exercise 4.6–4, $\alpha \cdot n = \alpha$ for every finite $n \neq 0$. One can also verify quite easily that $c \cdot n = c \cdot \alpha = c \cdot c = c$. For example, we obtain $c \cdot c = c$ from the fact that $E_2 = E_1 \times E_1$ and $E_2 \sim E_1$, while $\#(E_1) = c$. Finally, a very important law in finite arithmetic, the so-called product law, holds also for arbitrary cardinal numbers.

. . . .

THEOREM 5.7

$\mu \cdot \nu = 0$ if and only if $\mu = 0$ or $\nu = 0$ where μ and ν are cardinal numbers.

PROOF

If either $\mu = 0$ or $\nu = 0$ then $\mu \cdot \nu = 0$ by Exercise 5.4-9. Suppose $\mu \neq 0$ and $\nu \neq 0$ and let $\mu = \#(A)$, $\nu = \#(B)$. Then $A \neq \emptyset$ an l $B \neq \emptyset$ so that $A \times B \neq \emptyset$, and $\mu \cdot \nu = \#(A \times B) \neq 0$.   Q.E.D.

. . . .

Previous remarks about the futility of attempting to define subtraction apply equally well to division. A single example will reveal this. In finite arithmetic we define $n/m = k$, $m \neq 0$, if and only if $n = m \cdot k$, and we find that when k is defined it is unique. Moreover, $n/n = 1$ for every $n \neq 0$. Now $\alpha = \alpha \cdot 1$ so that we should have $\alpha/\alpha = 1$. On the other hand $\alpha = \alpha \cdot n$ so that $\alpha/\alpha = n$ for all $n \geq 1$.

In closing this section we should remark that it is possible to define a generalized product of cardinal numbers just as we defined a generalized sum. However, the definition requires the notion of a generalized Cartesian product which we do not wish to define at this time. The interested reader may consult Kamke, page 37 (see Bibliography).

. . . .

EXERCISES

1. Prove that addition of cardinal numbers is associative, i.e., $(\mu + \nu) + \rho = \mu + (\nu + \rho)$ where μ, ν, ρ are arbitrary cardinal numbers.

2. Show that $\nu + 0 = \nu$ for every cardinal ν.

3. Show the following:

    a. $c + n = c$ where n is finite.

    b. $c + c = c$.

    c. $c + n + \alpha = c$ where n is finite.

4. Show that if ν is any transfinite cardinal, then $\nu + \alpha = \nu$. (Hint: use Theorem 4.11).

5. Show that $\mu \cdot \nu = \nu \cdot \mu$ for any cardinals μ and ν, i.e., multiplication is commutative. (Hint: see Exercise 4.6–2).

6. Show that $\mu \cdot (\nu \cdot \rho) = (\mu \cdot \nu) \cdot \rho$ for any cardinals μ, ν, and ρ, i.e., multiplication is associative. (Hint: see Exercise 4.6–3).

7. Show that $\mu \cdot (\nu + \rho) = \mu \cdot \nu + \mu \cdot \rho$ for any cardinals μ, ν, and ρ, i.e., multiplication is distributive over addition. (Hint: see Exercise 3.3–4.)

8. Show that $\nu \cdot 1 = \nu$ for every cardinal ν. (Hint: see Exercise 4.6–1 and observe that $\#(\{0\}) = 1$).

9. Show that $\nu \cdot 0 = 0$ for every cardinal ν.

10. Show that $\mu \cdot \nu = 1$ if and only if $\mu = 1$ and $\nu = 1$.

5.5 POWERS OF CARDINAL NUMBERS

One method of approach to defining powers of cardinal numbers is revealed in the finite case whereby we define, for example, $2^3 = 2 \cdot 2 \cdot 2$ and, more generally, $m^n = m \cdot m \ldots m$ where there are n factors on the right of the equal sign. However, since we did not define a generalized product, this approach cannot be used here. Fortunately, there is another way to look at the problem although perhaps it is not as natural an approach. At any rate we find it gives us a satisfactory definition that will yield certain desirable properties.

Since our approach requires us to look outside the realm of previously defined operations, we turn once again to the meaning of m^n for finite sets in order to effect a general definition. We begin with an example. What meaning does 2^1 have for sets A and B with $2 = \#(A), 1 = \#(B)$? Well, we know the answer should be 2. Notice that if we let $B = \{a\}$, $A = \{0,1\}$, there are exactly two functions that can be defined from B to A, namely, $f = \{(a,0)\}$,

$g = \{(a,1)\}$. Thus, if we let $\mathfrak{F}$ denote the set of functions from B to A, $\#(\mathfrak{F}) = 2$. Let us explore this idea a little further. Let $B = \{a,b\}$ and $A = \{0,1\}$. How many functions are there with domain B and range a subset of A? They are $f_1 = \{(a,0), (b,0)\}$, $f_2 = \{(a,0), (b,1)\}, f_3 = \{(a,1), (b,0)\}$ and $f_4 = \{(a,1), (b,1)\}$. There are exactly four, which is 2^2.

More generally, then, suppose $m = \#(A)$ and $n = \#(B)$ where m and n are finite cardinal numbers. We may write $A = \{a_1, a_2, \ldots, a_m\}$ and $B = \{b_1, b_2, \ldots, b_n\}$. How many functions are there with domain B and range a subset of A? In order to define a function from B to A we must pair each element of B with one element of A (although two different b's may be paired with the same a), i.e., we must specify $f(b_k)$ as an element of A for $k = 1, 2, \ldots, n$. Let us begin with b_1. We can specify $f(b_1)$ in m distinct ways. Each of them defines a different function regardless of the values at $b_2, \ldots, b_n$ because at least one ordered pair (b_1, x) in each such function will be unique, that is, will not occur in any of the other functions so that the m functions thus defined are all distinct. (Remember, functions are sets of ordered pairs and hence two functions are unequal if they are unequal as sets, i.e., have at least one element in each which are not identical.)

Having determined m functions by specifying $f(b_1)$ we turn to $f(b_2)$ and argue as before that, independent of any previous or future assignments, there are m distinct ways to specify $f(b_2)$, hence m distinct such functions. We now have m^2 distinct functions. Proceeding in this manner, we arrive, in a finite number of steps, at a total of m^n such functions. This will be our guide in making a general definition.

Before giving our definition, we need some notation for the set of functions from B to A. To this end, we adopt, as did Cantor, the symbol B/A. Thus, in symbols, $B/A = \{f; f: B \longrightarrow A\}$. (Notice we do not need to specify in our set-builder notation that f is a function, for we agreed in Chapter 3 never to use the symbol $f: B \longrightarrow A$ unless f is a function with $\mathfrak{D}(f) = B$, $\mathfrak{R}(f) \subseteq A$.) Cantor called the set B/A a *covering* set, thinking of the elements of A as "covering" the elements of B by means of all the functions from B to A. Imitating the finite case we make the following general definition.

. . . .

DEFINITION 5.6

Let μ and ν be cardinal numbers. If $\mu = \#(A)$ and $\nu = \#(B)$ then $\mu^\nu = \#(B/A)$.

. . . .

A word of caution about using our definition. We write B first in the notation B/A since B is the domain of all functions in that set and it seems natural to write it first. But $\#(B)$ occurs in the exponent of μ^ν! So the student will have to be on guard and always remember that the set corresponding to the cardinal number in the exponent is always used to form the domain of the functions to be constructed.

There are certain natural consequences of our definition. As usual, the definition produces nothing new about exponents when μ and ν are finite, but this is not surprising. In general, though, we find our familiar laws of exponents holding even when μ or ν are transfinite. These properties are summarized in the next few theorems.

. . . .

THEOREM 5.8

(i) $\mu^1 = \mu$ for every cardinal μ.

(ii) $\mu^0 = 1$ for every cardinal μ.

(iii) If $\mu \neq 0$, $0^\mu = 0$.

PROOF

Let $\mu = \#(A)$, and $1 = \#(\{0\})$. For each $a \in A$ let f_a be a function on $\{0\}$ defined by $f_a(0) = a$. Then $f_a \in \{0\}/A$ for every $a \in A$ and $\{f_a; a \in A\} = \{0\}/A$. But clearly $\{f_a; a \in A\} \sim A$ under the map $\psi(f_a) = a$. Hence, $\mu^1 = \#(\{0\}/A) = \#(A) = \mu$ and (i) is proved.

Again with $\mu = \#(A)$ we first observe that if $f \in \varnothing/A$ then $f \subseteq \varnothing \times A = \varnothing$ so that $f = \varnothing$. Moreover $\mathfrak{D}(f) = \{x; x \in \varnothing, (x,y) \in f$ for some $y \in A\} = \varnothing$ and the statement "if $(x,y) \in f$ and $(x,z) \in f$ then $y = z$" is vacuously satisfied. Thus, $\varnothing: \varnothing \longrightarrow A$ and $\varnothing/A = \{\varnothing\}$ so that $\mu^0 = \#(\varnothing/A) = \#(\{\varnothing\}) = 1$ which proves (ii).

Finally, with $\mu = \#(A)$ and $A \neq \varnothing$, if $f \in A/\varnothing$ then $f \subseteq A \times \varnothing = \varnothing$ so that $f = \varnothing$. But then $\mathfrak{D}(f) = \{x; x \in A$ and $(x,y) \in f$ for some $y \in \varnothing\} = \varnothing \neq A$ and so $\varnothing$ is not a function from A to $\varnothing$ in this case. Since $f = \varnothing$ is the only possibility, $A/\varnothing = \varnothing$ and $0^\mu = \#(A/\varnothing) = \#(\varnothing) = 0$ which proves (iii). $\qquad$ Q.E.D.

. . . .

THEOREM 5.9

$\mu^{\nu+\rho} = \mu^\nu \cdot \mu^\rho$ for arbitrary cardinals μ, ν, and ρ.

PROOF

Let $\mu = \#(A)$, $\nu = \#(B)$, $\rho = \#(C)$ with $B \cap C = \varnothing$ so that $\nu + \rho = \#(B \cup C)$ in accordance with Definition 5.3. For each $f \in (B \cup C)/A$, let us define $F(f) = (f \mid B, f \mid C)$. Then $f \mid B: B \longrightarrow A$, $f \mid C: C \longrightarrow A$ so that $(f \mid B, f \mid C) \in B/A \times C/A$ and $F: (B \cup C)/A \longrightarrow B/A \times C/A$. We show that F is 1–1 and onto.

If $f,g \in (B \cup C)/A$ and $f \neq g$, then $f \mid B \neq g \mid B$ or $f \mid C \neq g \mid C$. (This is easy to verify—assume the contrary and find $f = g$.) Thus, $(f \mid B, f \mid C) \neq (g \mid B, g \mid C)$ or $F(f) \neq F(g)$ so that F is 1–1.

Suppose $(\varphi, \psi) \in B/A \times C/A$ is arbitrary. Then $\varphi: B \longrightarrow A$, $\psi: C \longrightarrow A$ and we let

$$f(x) = \begin{cases} \varphi(x) & \forall\ x \in B \\ \psi(x) & \forall\ x \in C \end{cases}$$

Since $B \cap C = \varnothing$, f is a function and $f: B \cup C \longrightarrow A$. But then $\varphi = f \mid B, \psi = f \mid C$ and $F(f) = (f \mid B, f \mid C) = (\varphi, \psi)$. Hence, F is onto.

Since F is 1–1 and onto, we have $(B \cup C)/A \sim B/A \times C/A$ so that $\mu^{\nu+\rho} = \#((B \cup C)/A) = \#(B/A \times C/A) = \#(B/A) \cdot \#(C/A) = \mu^\nu \cdot \mu^\rho$. $\qquad$ Q.E.D.

. . . .

THEOREM 5.10

$(\mu \cdot \nu)^\rho = \mu^\rho \cdot \nu^\rho$ for arbitrary cardinals μ, ν, ρ.

PROOF

Let $\mu = \#(A)$, $\nu = \#(B)$, $\rho = \#(C)$. For each $f \in C/(A \times B)$ we have $f(c) = (a,b)$ $\forall\, c \in C$ where $(a,b) \in A \times B$. Let $\varphi_f(c) = a$, $\psi_f(c) = b$. Then $\varphi_f\colon C \longrightarrow A$, $\psi_f\colon C \longrightarrow B$ and $(\varphi_f, \psi_f) \in C/A \times C/B$. Then define $F(f) = (\varphi_f, \psi_f)$ so that $F\colon C/(A \times B) \longrightarrow C/A \times C/B$. Suppose $f, g \in C/(A \times B)$ with $f \neq g$. If $(\varphi_f, \psi_f) = (\varphi_g, \psi_g)$ then $\varphi_f = \varphi_g$ and $\psi_f = \psi_g$ so that $f(c) = (\varphi_f(c), \psi_f(c)) = (\varphi_g(c), \psi_g(c)) = g(c)$ $\forall\, c \in C$, contrary to $f \neq g$. Thus, $F(f) = (\varphi_f, \psi_f) \neq (\varphi_g, \psi_g) = F(g)$ so that F is 1–1.

Let $(\varphi, \psi) \in C/A \times C/B$ be arbitrary so that $\varphi\colon C \longrightarrow A$ and $\psi\colon C \longrightarrow B$. Define $f(c) = (\varphi(c), \psi(c))$ $\forall\, c \in C$. Then, $f\colon C \longrightarrow A \times B$ and $\psi = \psi_f$, $\varphi = \varphi_f$ so that $F(f) = (\varphi_f, \psi_f) = (\varphi, \psi)$, i.e., F is onto. Since F is 1–1 and onto, $C/(A \times B) \sim C/A \times C/B$ so that $(\mu \cdot \nu)^\rho = \#(C/(A \times B)) = \#(C/A \times C/B) = \#(C/A) \cdot \#(C/B) = \mu^\rho \cdot \nu^\rho$. Q.E.D.

. . . .

THEOREM 5.11

$(\mu^\nu)^\rho = \mu^{\nu \cdot \rho}$ for arbitrary cardinals μ, ν, ρ.

PROOF

Let $\mu = \#(A)$, $\nu = \#(B)$, $\rho = \#(C)$. For each $f \in C/(B/A)$ we have $f(c) \in B/A$, i.e., $f(c)\colon B \longrightarrow A$ $\forall\, c \in C$. Denoting $f(c)$ by f_c we define, for each $(b,c) \in B \times C$, $h_f(b,c) = f_c(b)$. Then $h_f\colon B \times C \longrightarrow A$. Let $F(f) = h_f$ $\forall\, f \in C/(B/A)$ so that $F\colon C/(B/A) \longrightarrow (B \times C)/A$.

If $f, g \in C/(B/A)$ and $f \neq g$ then $f(c_0) \neq g(c_0)$ for some $c_0 \in C$, i.e., $f_{c_0} \neq g_{c_0}$. Also, $f_{c_0}(b_0) \neq g_{c_0}(b_0)$ for some $b_0 \in B$ and hence $h_f(b_0, c_0) = f_{c_0}(b_0) \neq g_{c_0}(b_0) = h_g(b_0,c_0)$. Then $h_f \neq h_g$ or $F(f) \neq F(g)$ so that F is 1–1.

Suppose $h \in (B \times C)/A$ is arbitrary. Define $h_c\colon B \longrightarrow A$ by $h_c(b) = h(b,c)$ $\forall\, (b,c) \in B \times C$. Then let $f(c) = h_c$. Accordingly, $f\colon C \longrightarrow B/A$ and $h_f(b,c) = f_c(b) = (f(c))(b) = h_c(b) = h(b,c)$ $\forall\, (b,c) \in B \times C$ so that $h_f = h$ and $F(f) = h$ whence F is onto.

Since F is 1–1 and onto, $C/(B/A) \sim (B \times C)/A$ and so $(\mu^\nu)^\rho = \#(C/(B/A)) = \#((B \times C)/A) = \mu^{\nu \cdot \rho}$. Q.E.D.

. . . .

Before turning to specific examples illustrating the use of the above theorems, we prove a very important theorem relating the power set of a set to cardinal exponentiation.

. . . .

THEOREM 5.12

Let $\nu = \#(A)$. Then $2^\nu = \#(p(A))$.

PROOF

Let $2 = \#(\{0,1\})$. Let $B \in p(A)$ (so that $B \subseteq A$) and define $\chi_B: A \longrightarrow \{0,1\}$ by

$$\chi_B(x) = \begin{cases} 0 \text{ if } x \in B \\ 1 \text{ if } x \in A - B \end{cases}$$

(The function χ_B is often called the *characteristic function* of the set B. Notice that $\chi_A \equiv 0$, $\chi_\varnothing \equiv 1$.) Now $\chi_B \in A/\{0,1\}$ $\forall$ $B \in p(A)$, so let $F(B) = \chi_B$ whence $F: p(A) \longrightarrow A/\{0,1\}$. Now if $B_1, B_2 \in p(A)$ and $B_1 \neq B_2$ then either there exists $x_0 \in A$ such that $x_0 \in B_1$ and $x_0 \notin B_2$ (hence $x_0 \in A - B_2$) or there is $x_1 \in A$ such that $x_1 \in B_2$ and $x_1 \notin B_1$. In the first case $\chi_{B_1}(x_0) = 0 \neq 1 = \chi_{B_2}(x_0)$, whereas in the second case $\chi_{B_1}(x_1) = 1 \neq 0 = \chi_{B_2}(x_1)$. Hence, $\chi_{B_1} \neq \chi_{B_2}$ or $F(B_1) \neq F(B_2)$ and F is 1–1.

Let $f \in A/\{0,1\}$ be arbitrary so that $f: A \longrightarrow \{0,1\}$. Let $B = \{x; f(x) = 0\}$. Then $B \subseteq A$ so that $B \in p(A)$ and, clearly, $f = \chi_B$ so that $F(B) = f$, i.e., F is onto.

Since F is 1–1 and onto, $A/\{0,1\} \sim p(A)$ so that $2^\nu = \#(A/\{0,1\}) = \#(p(A))$.   Q.E.D.

. . . .

COROLLARY

$2^\nu > \nu$ for every cardinal ν.

PROOF

Let $\nu = \#(A)$. Then, by Theorem 5.1, $\#(A) < \#(p(A))$ or $\nu < \#(p(A)) = 2^\nu$ by the theorem.   Q.E.D.

. . . .

As an immediate application of the last theorem, let us consider the set N/A where $A = \{0,1,2, \ldots ,9\}$ and N is the set of natural numbers. Each member of N/A is a function f whose image for each positive integer n is a number in set A. Suppose we let $F(f) = 0.f(1)f(2)f(3) \ldots$ for each $f \in N/A$. Then $F(f)$ is the decimal expansion of some number between zero and one for each f. However, we will have, in many cases, the situation where there is an integer k_0 such that $f(k) = 0$ for all $k \geq k_0$. Indeed, whenever $F(f)$ is a rational number such will be the case. For example, we might have $F(f) = 0.3124000 \ldots$. At the same time, suppose $F(g) = 0.3123999 \ldots$. Then $F(f)$ and $F(g)$ are decimal expansions of the same rational number. To get around this point, we agree to distinguish between $F(f)$ and $F(g)$ if $f(k) \neq g(k)$ for some $k \in N$. Then, let D be the set of all the above infinite decimal expansions having zeros from some decimal place on. Since such expansions are represented by rational numbers in the interval $[0,1) = \{x; x \in E_1, 0 \leq x < 1\}$, D is denumerable. Also, let E denote the set of all infinite decimal expansions which do not have zeros from some point on. We have seen in Chapter 4 that $E \sim [0,1]$ hence has cardinal c. Then $\#(D \cup E) = c$ and it is easy to verify that $F: N/A \xrightarrow[1-1]{\text{onto}} D \cup E$. Thus, $10^\alpha = \#(N/A) = \#(D \cup E) = c$.

Now the use of base 10 is completely irrelevant. That is, the members of $[0,1]$ also possess an expansion as above for any base $n > 1$ (where $n \in N$),* and a similar consideration shows that $n^\alpha = c$ for every finite cardinal n greater than 1. In particular, $2^\alpha = c$ and we have just seen that $2^\alpha = \#(p(A))$ for any denumerable set A, so we have:

The set of all subsets of a denumerable set has cardinal c.

The above theorems also provide some calculating techniques for computing powers of cardinal numbers. For example, if n is finite,

---

* For a particularly elegant proof of this theorem, see Patrick Suppes, *op. cit.*, p. 189.

$$c^n = (2^\alpha)^n = 2^{\alpha \cdot n} = 2^\alpha = c$$

$$c^\alpha = (2^\alpha)^\alpha = 2^{\alpha \cdot \alpha} = 2^\alpha = c$$

and

$$\alpha^\alpha = (2 \cdot \alpha)^\alpha = 2^\alpha \cdot \alpha^\alpha = 2^{\alpha \cdot \alpha} \cdot \alpha^\alpha =$$

$$(2^\alpha)^\alpha \cdot \alpha^\alpha = (2^\alpha \cdot \alpha)^\alpha = (c \cdot \alpha)^\alpha = c^\alpha = c$$

To conclude this chapter we state three theorems on inequalities, left as an exercise for the student, and show some applications. We can use the exercises to show, e.g., that $\alpha \cdot c = c$. Thus, $n < \alpha < c$ so that $n \cdot c \le \alpha \cdot c \le c \cdot c$. Hence, $c \le \alpha \cdot c \le c$ and we conclude $\alpha \cdot c = c$. To illustrate another use, $2 < \alpha < c$ so that $2^\alpha \le \alpha^\alpha \le c^\alpha$. But $2^\alpha = c^\alpha = c$ so we conclude that $\alpha^\alpha = c$.

. . . .

EXERCISES

1. Show that $c^c = 2^c$ and $n^c = 2^c$.

2. Let β, γ, μ, ν be cardinal numbers. If $\beta \le \mu$ and $\gamma \le \nu$ then,

   (i) $\beta + \gamma \le \mu + \nu$

   (ii) $\beta\gamma \le \mu\nu$

   (iii) $\beta^\gamma \le \mu^\nu$

3. Show that strict inequalities cannot be used in Exercise 5.5–2 by a counter-example.

4. Show that $\mu \le \mu + \nu$ for arbitrary cardinals μ and ν. Give a counter-example to show that strict inequality does not hold.

5. Prove that the function $F: N/A \longrightarrow D \cup E$, described above, is 1–1 and onto.

6

CONCLUSION

6.1 GENERAL REMARKS

With the closing of the preceding chapter, we achieved the goal which we set out to accomplish in the first chapter. That is, we have shown how the concept of number can be generalized from the finite to the transfinite in a systematic manner in keeping with the spirit of the axiomatic method. Moreover, a generalized arithmetic has been provided for those objects. But this is by no means all there is to the theory of sets.

In keeping with the purpose of this book, time and space prevent us from discussing the wide and varied applications of set theory. However, let us reiterate an earlier comment; namely, it is extremely unlikely that the reader will fail to see many applications of set theory if he pursues his study of mathematics beyond the present stage. We hope that in this regard he will have obtained many tools and techniques from his study of these materials which will be helpful in that pursuit.

Although the spirit of our presentation has been axiomatic, it has not been complete in the sense that it was necessary to postulate some results which do admit proof in a more complete axiomatic treatment. Sometimes this was done because our assumptions were insufficient to effect a proof. At other times it was felt that the proof was too involved to present at this level and would cause a delay in our progress.

In spite of the above remarks, we feel obligated to discuss some of these matters further, hoping that the interested student will find more detail on the subject in one or more of the references cited in the bibliography. To this end we will deal with matters less formally than we have to this point, pausing only to give the definitions of the terms involved and usually a heuristic discussion of the main results.

6.2 ORDERED SETS

We begin as usual by examining finite sets. The elementary pupil, in studying arithmetic, soon learns that a natural number is used in two different senses. On the one hand, it is used in a cardinal or counting sense, whereby it may be thought of as simply counting the number of elements in a set. We have in fact abstracted that property of natural numbers in the preceding chapters. On the other hand, another meaning for natural number is embodied in the words "first," "second," "third," etc., whereby a definite ordering of the objects of a set is implied. Hence, we would like to first of all make the notion of such an ordering precise and then abstract the property from finite sets to infinite sets.

Our intuitive concept of order does not apply to the empty set nor to a set containing a single element. That is, we need to have at least two elements in a set before we can begin to speak of order in any intuitive sense. We may then either omit the empty set and singleton sets from our discussion or consider them ordered in a vacuous sense. Most authors adopt the second alternative in order to make quite general statements about ordered sets when those sets are finite.

Let us examine a set which contains precisely two elements such as $A = \{a,b\}$ where we assume $a \neq b$. To specify an ordering of the elements of A, it is clear that all we must do is say which element is to be considered as "first" and which as "second." There are two ways that we can do this. We can say a is first and b is second or b is first and a is second. But we have faced this problem before (see Chapter 3), and we found that the notion of ordered pair solved the problem very nicely. Thus, in the notation (a,b), we may say a is first and b is second or a precedes b in contrast to the ordering (b,a) where b precedes a.

In the more general situation, the set A will have more than just two elements. How should we define an ordering of A? First and foremost, it occurs to us that any reasonable definition that coincides with our intuitive notion of ordering should require that if x and y are two different elements of A, we should be able to say that either x precedes y or y precedes x. But now we are back to pairs of elements and we are reminded of the ordered pairs (x,y) and (y,x) to denote this idea of precedence. Since relations in A, i.e., subsets of $A \times A$, are sets of ordered pairs whose coordinates are elements of A, it would appear that fundamentally an ordering of a set A is a relation r in A where we agree that $(x,y) \in r$ means x precedes y.

Now an arbitrary relation r in A will not determine an ordering because there are certain properties which we intuitively feel such a relation should possess. For instance, it is contrary to our intuition to say x precedes x for any $x \in A$; that is, $(x,x) \notin r$ for any $x \in A$ (in contrast with the reflexive property of an equivalence relation). Also, if x precedes y we would require that y does not precede x or if $(x,y) \in r$ then $(y,x) \notin r$ (in contrast with the symmetric property of an equivalence relation). If x precedes y and y precedes z, it seems natural to require that x precede z, which is to say if $(x,y) \in r$ and $(y,z) \in r$ then $(x,z) \in r$, i.e., r is transitive. If we were to list more properties to be required of r we might discover that some are consequences of others, which would suggest shortening the list of requirements for r. One such list occurs below in our definition which incorporates these ideas.

· ·

DEFINITION 6.1

Let A be a set. An *ordering relation in A* is a relation r in A satisfying:

(i) If $x \in A$ then $(x,x) \notin r$. (*r is irreflexive*)

(ii) If $x,y \in A$ and $x \neq y$, then $(x,y) \in r$ or $(y,x) \in r$. (*r is connective*)

(iii) r is *transitive*.

· ·

Having decided on what we mean by an ordering of a set, what shall we mean by the term "ordered set"? The answer seems natural enough: an ordered set is a set together with an ordering of that set (where ordering means an ordering relation of course). To complete the answer we should be able to distinguish between ordered sets. It seems reasonable to say that two ordered sets are equal if and only if the sets involved are equal and the ordering relations are also equal. But this kind of equality between pairs of objects is taken care of by the notion of ordered pair. This prompts our definition.

· ·

DEFINITION 6.2

An *ordered set* is an ordered pair (A,r) in which A is a set and r is an ordering relation in A.

· ·

Observe that the definition establishes the equality referred to above very nicely so that, by definition of ordered pairs, if (A,r) and (B,t) are ordered sets, then $(A,r) = (B,t) \Leftrightarrow A = B$ and $r = t$ (as sets, of course).

Before giving some examples, it is only fair to warn the reader that most authors use the symbol $<$ (not to be confused with ordinary $<$ for real numbers except when this is intended) to represent an arbitrary ordering relation, rather than r. We shall use both and have preferred to begin the way we have in order to make the student aware that we are using familiar notions previously defined. Also, instead of $(x,y) \in \, <$ most writers prefer $x < y$, which is perhaps a more natural translation of the phrase "x precedes y." But there is a little loss in this because the fact that $<$ is a relation, hence a set of ordered pairs, is not emphasized. Finally, many authors simply suppress the relation r altogether and speak of the ordered set A. There is a great danger in this because, of course, the ordering relation is really the most important part of the concept of ordered set and, except for special examples when the ordering is clearly understood, the beginning student is often confused by the omission.*

As a first example, let us observe that when we write $N = \{1,2,3, \ldots\}$ we have in mind that the natural numbers are written in their natural order, which is to say that the next entry following the last comma is 4. But this is merely a device and we emphasized in preceding chapters that the order is immaterial from the point of view of representing the set N. If we are interested in emphasizing the order we might agree that $<$ is the ordering relation in N whereupon the above listing represents the ordered set $(N,<)$. Nevertheless, it is helpful to visualize the ordering for a few elements. We might agree then to use the notation $\{1,2,3, \ldots\}$ to represent the set and the ordering, but we should not and will not

---

* As an added note of caution, the reader should be told that not all authors use the same definition of an ordering relation as we have given in Definition 6.1. Some give definitions that are equivalent, others do not. All we can say is that different definitions serve different purposes, and in reading other materials one should always check on the definitions for the terms used.

equate $(N,<)$ to this representation. Instead, let us adopt the symbol $\leftrightarrow$ to be read "is represented by" and write $(N,<) \leftrightarrow \{1,2,3,\ldots\}$.

Another natural ordering of N is given by $x > y$. Then we have $(N,>) \leftrightarrow \{\ldots, 3,2,1\}$. Others that we might consider are $(Z,<) \leftrightarrow \{\ldots, -1,0,1,\ldots\}$, $(Z,>) \leftrightarrow \{\ldots, 1,0,-1,\ldots\}$ and $(R,<)$, $(E_1,>)$. In all of these cases, we call $>$ and $<$ natural orderings. Let us examine some unnatural ones. In N, let us define the relation r_1 by $(x,y) \in r_1 \Leftrightarrow (x,y$ are odd and $x < y)$ or $(x,y$ are even and $x < y)$ or $(x$ is odd and y is even). Then $(N,r_1) \leftrightarrow \{1,3,5,\ldots,2,4,6,\ldots\}$. In R^+ suppose $(m/n,p/q) \in r_2 \Leftrightarrow (n < q)$ or $(n = q$ and $m < p)$. Then we would have $(R^+,r_2) \leftrightarrow \{\frac{1}{1},\frac{2}{1},\frac{3}{1},\ldots, \frac{1}{2},\frac{3}{2},\frac{5}{2},\ldots, \frac{1}{3},\frac{2}{3},\frac{4}{3},\ldots\}$.

If (A,r) is an ordered set and $B \subseteq A$, there is a natural way to order B by means of r. Let us define $r' = \{(x,y); (x,y) \in r$ and $x,y \in B\}$. It is easy to verify that r' is an ordering relation, and we will call it the *ordering relation restricted to B*. The idea is that (B,r') is an ordered set with the order of the elements, as elements of A, preserved. Of course if $B = A$, then $r' = r$.

6.3 SIMILARITY AND WELL-ORDERED SETS

In our examples we notice that $(N,<) \neq (N,>)$, even though N is involved in both cases. Observe that $< \neq >$ since $(x,y) \in < \Leftrightarrow (y,x) \in >$. Also, $(Z,<) \neq (N,<)$ since $Z \neq N$ even though $Z \sim N$. A notion for ordered sets which parallels somewhat the concept of equivalence for sets is given below.

· ·

DEFINITION 6.3

Let (A,r) and (B,t) be ordered sets. Then (A,r) is *similar* to (B,t), denoted $(A,r) \simeq (B,t)$, if there exists $f: A \longrightarrow B$ satisfying:

(i) $A \sim B$ under f, i.e., $f: A \xrightarrow[1-1]{onto} B$.

(ii) If $(x,y) \in r$ then $(f(x),f(y)) \in t$.

. . . .

In (ii) of the definition we notice that if x precedes y in A then $f(x)$ precedes $f(y)$ in B. For this reason f is called *order-preserving*. Also, we often call f a *similarity mapping*. As an example, consider the ordered sets $(N,<)$ and $(E,<) \leftrightarrow \{2,4,6, \ldots\}$. The function $f(x) = 2x$ is clearly a similarity mapping of N onto E so that $(N,<) \simeq (E,<)$. We leave it to the reader to verify that $\simeq$ determines an equivalence relation in any set of ordered sets, i.e., $(A,r) \simeq (A,r)$, $(A,r) \simeq (B,t) \Rightarrow (B,t) \simeq (A,r)$ while $(A,r) \simeq (B,t)$ and $(B,t) \simeq (C,u) \Rightarrow (A,r) \simeq (C,u)$.

The concepts of first and last elements of an ordered set are sometimes quite helpful in distinguishing ordered sets.

. . . .

DEFINITION 6.4

Let (A,r) be an ordered set. Then,

(i) $a \in A$ is a *first element* if $(a,x) \in r \forall x \in A$ with $x \neq a$.

(ii) $b \in A$ is a *last element* if $(x,b) \in r \forall x \in A$ with $x \neq b$.

. . . .

We then can prove the following theorem.

. . . .

THEOREM 6.1

Let (A,r) and (B,t) be similar ordered sets with f mapping A onto B. Then,

(i) a is a first element of $(A,r) \Rightarrow f(a)$ is a first element of (B,t).

(ii) b is a last element of $(A,r) \Rightarrow f(b)$ is a last element of (B,t).

PROOF

Suppose a is a first element of (A,r). Let $y \in B$ with $y \neq f(a)$. Then $\exists x \in A \ni y = f(x)$ and $x \neq a$ since f is 1–1. Also, $(a,x) \in r \Rightarrow$

$(f(a),f(x)) \in t$ since f is order-preserving, i.e., $(f(a),y) \in t \; \forall \; y \in B$ with $y \neq f(a)$ so that $f(a)$ is a first element of (B,t), which proves (i). The proof of (ii) is left to the reader. Q.E.D.

. . . .

As an immediate application of the theorem, observe that $(N,<)$ and $(N,>)$ cannot be similar sets since the former has a first element and the latter does not. Also, the sets $(N,<)$ and $(Z,<)$ are not similar for the same reason. However, if we were to re-order Z using the representation $\{0,1,-1,2,-2,\ldots\}$, it would appear that the resulting ordered set would be similar to $(N,<)$. This suggests the following general theorem.

. . . .

THEOREM 6.2

Let (A,r) be an ordered set and suppose $B \sim A$. Then there is an ordering relation r^* in B such that $(A,r) \simeq (B,r^*)$.

PROOF

Let $f: A \xrightarrow[1-1]{\text{onto}} B$. Define $(u,v) \in r^* \Leftrightarrow u = f(x), \quad v = f(y)$ and $(x,y) \in r$. It is easy to verify that r^* is an ordering relation and, by construction of r^*, f is order-preserving. Q.E.D.

. . . .

In the theorem, we sometimes call r^* the *order relation induced by r and f*. As an application, let us return to the example preceding the theorem. The function

$$f(x) = \begin{cases} 0 \text{ if } x = 1 \\ y \text{ if } x = 2y \\ -y \text{ if } x = 2y + 1 \end{cases} \quad \forall \; x \in N$$

establishes $N \sim Z$. Accordingly, $(N,<) \simeq (Z,< *)$ and $(Z,< *) \leftrightarrow \{0,1,-1,2,-2,\ldots\}$. Notice that 1 is a first element in $(N,<)$ and $f(1) = 0$ is a first element in $(Z,< *)$ as it must be under similarity. Thus, although equivalent sets with arbitrary orderings do not, in general, determine similar sets, one of them may always be re-ordered so that the resulting ordered sets are similar.

Ordered sets having first elements are of special significance, and we separate them from others by means of the following definition.

. . . .

DEFINITION 6.5

Let (A,r) be an ordered set. Then (A,r) is said to be *well-ordered* if (A',r') has a first element for every non-empty subset, A', of A.†

. . . .

It is easy to see that the ordered sets $(N,<)$, $(Z,< *) \leftrightarrow \{0,1,-1,2,-2,\ldots\}$, $(N,r) \leftrightarrow \{1,3,5,\ldots,2,4,6,\ldots\}$ are all well-ordered. Also, the sets $(N,>)$ and $(Z,<)$ are clearly not well-ordered since neither has a first element. Of course, even if an ordered set has a first element, we have no guarantee that it is well-ordered. For example, the ordered set $([0,1],<)$ is an ordered set and has a first element, namely, 0. But the subset $U = \{x; 0 < x < 1\}$, as the ordered set $(U,< ')$ does not have a first element. The ordered set $(R^+,<)$, where R^+ is the set of non-negative rationals, is a similar example.

Some theorems are immediate consequences of the definition and are not difficult to prove.

. . . .

THEOREM 6.3

If (A,r) is a well-ordered set and $A' \subseteq A$, then (A',r') is a well-ordered set.

PROOF

Left to the reader.

. . . .

---

† As previously defined, r' is the ordering relation r restricted to A'.

THEOREM 6.4

If (A,r) is a well-ordered set and $(B,t) \simeq (A,r)$, then (B,t) is well-ordered.

PROOF

Suppose $B' \subseteq B$. Let $f: B \longrightarrow A$ be a similarity mapping of B onto A. Then clearly $f \mid B'$ is a similarity mapping of B' onto a subset A' of A and, since (A',r') has a first element by hypothesis, (B',t') has a first element by Theorem 6.1. Since B' was arbitrary, (B,t) is well-ordered. Q.E.D.

. . . .

The most important theorem about well-ordered sets, and one of the deepest in set theory, is the well-ordering theorem first proved by Zermelo in 1904. The statement of the theorem is simple enough but the proof is certainly beyond the scope of this text.

. . . .

THEOREM 6.5

(Well-ordering Theorem.) Every set can be well-ordered.

PROOF

Not given.

. . . .

Although the theorem assures us that if A is any set, we can find an ordering relation r in A such that (A,r) is a well-ordered set, unfortunately the proof does not give us a means of actually constructing r. And today there are still sets, such as those with cardinal c, which we know can be well-ordered, but no one has been able to show an ordering relation which will accomplish this.

6.4 ORDINAL NUMBERS

Putting the last two theorems together, if A is any set it can be well-ordered and any other set similar to it is also well-ordered.

In the same way that we defined cardinal number from the notion of equivalence of sets, we now define ordinal number from similarity of well-ordered sets.

. . . .

DEFINITION 6.6

Let (A,r) be a well-ordered set. The *ordinal number* of (A,r), denoted $[(A,r)]$, is a primitive notion with the property that $[(A,r)] = [(B,t)] \Leftrightarrow (A,r) \simeq (B,t).$*

. . . .

Let us observe that every finite set is trivially well-ordered. Moreover, if $A = \{a_1, a_2, \ldots, a_k\}$ is an arbitrary finite set, there are exactly $k!$ orderings of A and the resulting sets are all similar. In addition, any other set with cardinal k together with an arbitrary ordering of its elements will also be similar to A. Thus, the ordinal number is the same for all these sets. This number can be expressed by k, for we can consider the last element (which must exist) in any of these ordered sets as the kth. In this sense, k serves the double duty of representing both a finite cardinal number and a finite ordinal number. The case of the empty set and a singleton set is a little bothersome as we mentioned before because ordering of their elements has no intuitive meaning. We assume that they are well-ordered sets and admit the corresponding cardinal numbers 0 and 1 as ordinal numbers for the sake of consistency.

In a like manner, but with a great deal of ambiguity, we shall denote arbitrary ordinal numbers by Greek letters and we assume: μ is an ordinal number (or, more briefly, ordinal) $\Leftrightarrow$ there exists a well-ordered set (A,r) with $\mu = [(A,r)]$. We will reserve ω for the set $(N,<)$ so that $\omega = [(N,<)]$. The ambiguity arises from the fact that, although there is a one-to-one correspondence between finite ordinals and finite cardinals, and to a given ordinal there corresponds a unique cardinal, it happens that to a given transfinite cardinal there will correspond many ordinals. Since we will

---

* See footnote, p. 126.

not explore ordinal number theory in great detail, the ambiguity will not be pronounced.

As in cardinal number theory, one of our first considerations is the matter of comparability of ordinal numbers. For this purpose, the concept of section is useful.

. . . .

DEFINITION 6.7

Let (A,r) be an ordered set and $m \in A$. The *m-section of* A, denoted A_m, is defined by $A_m = \{x; (x,m) \in r\}$.

. . . .

Since A_m is a subset of A we may, by restricting r to A_m, form the ordered set (A_m,r'). Also, we note that $m \notin A_m$.

Generally speaking, an ordered set may be similar to one of its sections (as an ordered set, of course). For instance, if $(N,r) \leftrightarrow \{\ldots,3,2,1\}$ we have $(N_1,r') \leftrightarrow \{\ldots,4,3,2\}$ and $(N,r) \simeq (N_1,r')$ under the similarity mapping $f(x) = x + 1 \; \forall \; x \in N$. Also, it is possible to have two ordered sets which are neither similar nor is one similar to a segment of the other as, for example, $(N,<) \leftrightarrow \{1,2,3,\ldots\}$ and $(N,>) \leftrightarrow \{\ldots,3,2,1\}$. It should be clear, however, that this is not the case for well-ordered sets. No well-ordered set can be similar to one of its sections. This should be intuitively obvious from the fact that an order-preserving mapping must map first element into first element, second element into second element, and so forth. But even more important is the following theorem which we give without proof.

. . . .

THEOREM 6.6

If (A,r) and (B,t) are well-ordered sets, then either they are similar or one of them is similar to a section of the other.

PROOF

Not given.

. . . .

To see the importance of the theorem, let us adopt the following criterion for ordering ordinal numbers.

. . . .

DEFINITION 6.8

Let $\mu = [(A,r)]$ and $\nu = [(B,t)]$. Then $\mu < \nu \Leftrightarrow (A,r) \simeq (B_m,t)$ for some section B_m of B.

. . . .

Then, according to Theorem 6.6, if μ and ν are arbitrary ordinal numbers then $\mu = \nu$ or if $\mu \neq \nu$ then either $\mu < \nu$ or $\nu < \mu$. Thus, ordinal numbers are comparable.

In more extensive treatments of ordered sets the notion of *order type* of an arbitrary ordered set is introduced. This may be done by relaxing the requirement in Definition 6.6 that the set be well-ordered. Then an ordinal number is the order type of a well-ordered set. From our remarks preceding Theorem 6.6 it is clear that order types would not be comparable, hence the reason for not calling them "numbers." The various theorems and properties of order types constitutes an interesting study with corresponding important applications. We have by-passed this notion in an effort to be brief and yet cover the main results. For more extensive treatments the reader should consult the bibliography.

Again, for the sake of brevity, we shall not discuss in any detail the rather extensive arithmetic of ordinal numbers together with their ramifications. Rather, we pause only to define addition and point out one or two results in that regard.

. . . .

DEFINITION 6.9

Let $\mu = [(A,r)]$ and $\nu = [(B,t)]$ with $A \cap B = \emptyset$. Then the *sum* of μ and ν, denoted $\mu + \nu$, is defined by $\mu + \nu = [(A \cup B, s)]$ where $(x,y) \in s \Leftrightarrow (x,y) \in r$ or $(x,y) \in t$ or $(x \in A$ and $y \in B)$.

. . . .

The reader should show that the relation s defined in Definition 6.9 is indeed an ordering relation and that $(A \cup B, s)$ is a well-ordered set. These details are omitted and, when verified, show that at least $\mu + \nu$ will be an ordinal number, which is desirable.

Intuitively, the relation s, defined above, is one which forces us to regard the elements of A first in the order in which they occur and then follow these elements with the elements of B in the order in which they occur. Then each element of A precedes every element of B while the order of two elements in A (and in B) is preserved. For example, if $(A,r) \leftrightarrow \{1,3,5, \ldots\}$ and $(B,t) \leftrightarrow \{2,4,6, \ldots\}$ then $(A \cup B,s) \leftrightarrow \{1,3,5, \ldots, 2,4,6, \ldots\}$. By the way, since $\omega = [(A,r)]$ and $\omega = [(B,t)]$, we have displayed $\omega + \omega$.

From the nature of our definition of addition we would not expect it to be a commutative operation. To see this, let us examine $\omega + 1$ and $1 + \omega$. Representing 1 by $\{0\}$ and ω by $(N,<)$ we would have $1 + \omega$ represented by $\{0,1,2,3, \ldots\}$, which is clearly similar to $(N,<)$, i.e., $1 + \omega = \omega$. But $\omega + 1$ would be represented by $\{1,2,3, \ldots, 0\}$ which is not similar to $(N,<)$ since the latter has no last element. Thus, $1 + \omega \neq \omega + 1$. Also, notice that if $(B,r) \leftrightarrow \{1,2,3, \ldots, 0\}$ then $(N,<) \simeq (B_0,r')$, i.e., $(N,<)$ is similar to a section of B. Accordingly, $\omega < \omega + 1$. Similar investigations (the reader should attempt some) yield a wide succession of ordinal numbers ordered according to magnitude. Some of these are indicated as follows:

$$0 < 1 < \ldots < \omega < \omega + 1 < \omega + 2 < \ldots < \omega + \omega <$$
$$\omega + \omega + 1 < \omega + \omega + 2 < \ldots < \omega + \omega + \omega < \ldots$$

The sketchy treatment of ordered sets and ordinal numbers presented here should in no way be taken as an indication of the relative importance of the subject. Indeed, from many points of view, ordinal number theory is far more extensive, and inherently more difficult, than the theory of cardinal numbers. A more extensive treatment, on the other hand, would soon take us beyond the level and scope intended. At any rate, we hope that enough

of the basic definitions and concepts have been presented here for the interested reader to profitably undertake further study.

6.5   AXIOM OF CHOICE

At several points in our development we found it necessary to state a theorem without proof.   This was done because we honestly felt that the proof was truly beyond the scope of the text and, if given, would cause a serious delay in progress.   At some of these points, the difficulty arises from the fact that the only proofs available involve an assumption which was deliberately omitted from the start.   That assumption is called the Axiom of Choice and is stated as follows.

. . . .

AXIOM OF CHOICE

If A is any non-empty set, then there exists a function f with the properties:

(i) $\mathcal{D}(f) = p(A) - \{\varnothing\}$

(ii) $f(B) \in B \; \forall \; B \in \mathcal{D}(f)$

. . . .

In words, the Axiom of Choice thus states that for any non-empty set A, it is possible to find a function f which selects a unique element from each non-empty subset of A.   For this reason, f is often called a *choice function*.   Now for finite sets, as usual, there is no problem.   For example, if $A = \{a, b\}$ then there are precisely two distinct choice functions f_1 and f_2 given by $f_1(\{a\}) = a$, $f_1(\{b\}) = b, f_1(A) = a$ and $f_2(\{a\}) = a, f_2(\{b\}) = b, f_2(A) = b$.   It should be clear that for any finite set A such functions exist and indeed there are only a finite number of such functions.   The reader may find it interesting to determine just how many.

The trouble arises when A is infinite. For then such a function must select an infinite number of elements of A simultaneously, and it is not a priori certain that such a choice can be made. By this time the reader should be quite aware of the fact that when dealing with infinite sets some properties do not follow as expected. At any rate it does not seem to be possible to prove the assertion of the Axiom of Choice as a theorem within the axiomatic structure of set theory without assuming some statement that is tautologically equivalent to it, and hence it must be postulated. By the way, the reader should observe that there is a very important difference, though perhaps a little subtle, in statements like "let $x \in A$" and the Axiom of Choice. The former, of course, was used many times in our proofs and, if $A \neq \varnothing$ the very definition of $\varnothing$ guarantees the existence of $x \in A$, and we have thereby selected a single element. Again, the difficulty arises when an infinity of choices must be made, all at the same time.

Perhaps it would be well to point out where the axiom is needed to prove theorems in this text. We mentioned in Chapter 4 (page 102) that Dedekind's definition of an infinite set was equivalent to our definition, and we used this fact at many points in the text thereafter. It is easy to show that if a set is (Dedekind) infinite then it is infinite in our sense. The proof of the converse requires the axiom. Then the trichotomy law for cardinal numbers was accepted without proof; again, the axiom is needed. Finally, Zermelo assumed the axiom in proving the well-ordering theorem.

Of course, the above results are extremely important in our theory, and we are not aware of any proofs of these results without employing the axiom. Indeed, the well-ordering theorem, as well as the trichotomy law for cardinal numbers, turns out to be tautologically equivalent to the Axiom of Choice. Thus, if any of these is assumed as an axiom, the others can be derived as theorems. The axiom has become such a pastime for mathematicians that the list of statements, all tautologically equivalent to the Axiom of Choice, and drawn from various branches of mathematics, has grown to a respectable size.

By this time perhaps the reader is wondering why such an issue is being made over another axiom when we certainly have not hesitated to introduce them before when they were needed. But the situation here is not so simple. The great mathematician Gödel was able to show that the addition of this axiom into our framework will not lead to a contradiction. We call such a property of axioms *consistency*. But consistency is not the only requirement we impose on axioms before admitting them, and whether or not the Axiom of Choice satisfies other requirements is still open to question. Let it be said that at this writing the question is unresolved.

A common feeling that has appeared to develop in contemporary mathematics is this: When a proof for a theorem can be given without using the Axiom of Choice, give it; otherwise, proofs using the Axiom should be clearly labeled as such and at least some confidence may be taken in the fact that the theorem cannot be a contradiction.

6.6 THE RUSSELL PARADOX

Now that the reader has developed what we hope is a certain degree of confidence in set theory as an axiomatic mathematical system, it might be well before leaving the subject to shake that confidence slightly. Perhaps the discussion of the last section made the reader somewhat uneasy about the subject, but even there we observed that we could not arrive at a contradiction with the assumption of the Axiom of Choice, and that should restore some confidence. We now turn to a final issue which has yet to be resolved.

In Cantor's so-called definition of set, the word "definite" appears in connection with objects, the collection of which are supposed to constitute a set. Of course, as we have indicated, Cantor did not establish an axiomatic framework for set theory.

At any rate, when attempts are made to formalize his writings into an axiomatic framework, the word "definite" tacitly implies in one way or another that there should be at hand a set of all objects. In order to decide set membership for a given set, all objects should be considered (in spirit anyway) and verified as either belonging or not belonging to the set in question.

Shortly after Cantor's works were published, the famous English philosopher Bertrand Russell discovered that the admission of a set of all sets would lead to a contradiction. We state one form of this paradox as a theorem.

. . . .

THEOREM 6.7

There does not exist a set of all sets.

PROOF

Suppose α were such a set. Then if A is any set, $A \in \alpha$. Now the property $P(A)$: $A \notin A$ is certainly a meaningful property for elements of α.* Let $M = \{A; A \in \alpha, A \notin A\}$. By the Axiom of Specification M is a set, hence $M \in \alpha$, and by the law of the excluded middle $M \in M$ or $M \notin M$.

But if $M \in M$ then, by definition, $M \in \alpha$ and $M \notin M$ so that $M \in M$ and $M \notin M$, which is a contradiction.

On the other hand, if $M \notin M$ then this is so only if $M \notin \alpha$ or $M \in M$. But $M \in \alpha$ so that we must have $M \in M$. Thus, $M \notin M$ and $M \in M$, which is a contradiction.

In either case, a contradiction arises so that α does not exist. Q.E.D.

. . . .

The paradox arises from admitting α as a set of all sets, of course. The reason we can state and prove the above result as a theorem is because of the Axiom of Specification. In turn, the latter axiom, in a manner of speaking, obtains a refinement from

---

* Indeed, every set which we have treated in the preceding chapters have this property. We made an issue, for example, over the distinction between $\{a\}$ and a whereby $\{a\} \notin \{a\}$.

the paradox. That is to say, in the Axiom of Specification we have asserted that we must have a set A to begin with as well as a meaningful statement about the elements of A. Without the condition of having a set first, we would have to admit into existence certain sets which would lead to contradictions.*

Russell's paradox was not the only one to arise in set theory. Indeed, others were discovered earlier than his. The result of all of these paradoxes was a serious attempt to refine axioms in such a way as to avoid the paradoxes and, at the same time, preserve the main body of results. That all of these issues have not been settled has been mentioned before.

In summary, let us reiterate that set theory has provided for us a new field of interest in mathematics, one which, in addition to its own peculiar properties, paved the way for the development of new mathematics through its use as a tool. To what extent set theory will continue to play this role is hard to say. But it can hardly be said that interest is lacking when one views the activity and controversy created by the subject.

---

* For further discussion, consult the references in the bibliography.

APPENDIX

No set N_k can be equivalent to a proper subset of itself.

PROOF

We will proceed by mathematical induction. The only proper subset of N_1 is $\emptyset$ and certainly it is not true that $\emptyset \sim N_1$ so that the statement is true for $k = 1$. Assume it is true for N_m and consider the set $N_{m+1} = N_m \cup \{m + 1\}$. Suppose N_{m+1} is equivalent to some proper subset A, i.e., $A \subset N_{m+1}$ and $N_{m+1} \sim A$ under the 1–1 correspondence f. We will arrive at a contradiction as follows: Since $f: N_{m+1} \xrightarrow[1-1]{\text{onto}} A$, let $a = f(m + 1)$ and $B = A - \{a\}$. Three cases then arise.

CASE I: $a = m + 1$

If $x \in B$ then $x \in A$ but $x \neq a = m + 1$ so that $x \in N_{m+1}$ and $x \neq m + 1$ which means $x \in N_m$. Thus, since x was arbitrary,

$B \subset N_m$. Let $g = f \mid N_m$, i.e., $g(x) = f(x) \; \forall \; x \in N_m$. Then $g: N_m \longrightarrow A$ and is 1–1. If $y \in B$, $y \in A$ so that $\exists \; x \in N_{m+1}$ such that $f(x) = y$ since f is onto. But $y \neq f(m + 1)$ so $x \neq m + 1$ since f is 1–1 so that $x \in N_m$ and $g(x) = f(x)$. Thus, if $y \in B$, $\exists \; x \in N_m$ such that $y = g(x)$, which says $\mathfrak{R}(g) = B$ so that $g: N_m \xrightarrow[1-1]{\text{onto}} B$ and $N_m \sim B$, with $B \subset N_m$, contrary to the inductive assumption.

CASE 2: $a \neq m + 1$ and $m + 1 \notin B$

In this case $m + 1 \notin A$ so, as above, $B \subset N_m$. Using again $g = f \mid N_m$, g is 1–1 and maps N_m onto B, contrary to our inductive assumption.

CASE 3: $a \neq m + 1$ and $m + 1 \in B$

Now $m + 1 \in A$ and hence there is $x_0 \in N_{m+1}$ such that $m + 1 = f(x_0)$ since f is onto. Let us define

$$\varphi(x) = \begin{cases} m + 1 & \text{if } x = m + 1 \\ a & \text{if } x = x_0 \\ f(x) & \text{if } x \in N_{m+1} - (\{m + 1\} \cup \{x_0\}) \end{cases}$$

Then $\varphi(x)$ is defined for each $x \in N_{m+1}$ and $\varphi: N_{m+1} \longrightarrow A$. It may be verified that φ is 1–1 and onto. So we let $a' = \varphi(m + 1)$ and $B' = A - \{a'\}$. Then $a' = m + 1$ and Case 1 applies with φ instead of f and a contradiction of the inductive hypothesis is obtained.

Thus, in all cases, we arrive at a contradiction so we conclude N_{m+1} cannot be equivalent to a proper subset. By mathematical induction, the theorem is true. Q.E.D.

Note: The preceding proof is essentially that given in Wilder (page 68, see Bibliography) with many of the details supplied.

GLOSSARY OF SYMBOLS

$<$	less than
$\leq$	less than or equal to
$\lvert x \rvert$	the absolute value of x
$\lim\limits_{x \to 0} f(x)$	the limit of $f(x)$ as x approaches zero
$\forall$	for each (for all, for every)
$\exists$	there exist(s)
$\ni$	such that
$- p$	not p
$\wedge$	and
$\vee$	or
$\Rightarrow$	implies
$\Leftrightarrow$	if and only if
$a \in A$	a is an element of A

$a \notin A$	a is not an element of A
$\{x; p(x)\}$	the set of all x such that $p(x)$
$\{a,b,c\}$	the set consisting of the elements a, b, and c
N	the set of natural numbers
Z	the set of integers
R	the set of rational numbers
E_1	the set of real numbers
C	the set of complex numbers
$A \subseteq B$	A is a subset of B
$A \nsubseteq B$	A is not a subset of B
$A \subset B$	A is a proper subset of B
$\varnothing$	the empty set
$p(A)$	the set of all subsets of set A, the power set of A
$A \cup B$	the union of sets A and B
$A \cap B$	the intersection of sets A and B
$\bigcup_{t \in T} C_t$	the union of the sets C_t where $t \in T$
$\bigcap_{t \in T} C_t$	the intersection of the sets C_t where $t \in T$
$\bigcap_{k=1}^{n} C_k$	the intersection of sets $C_1, C_2, \ldots, C_n$
$\bigcup_{k=1}^{n} C_k$	the union of sets $C_1, C_2, \ldots, C_n$
(a,b)	the ordered pair a, b
$A \times B$	Cartesian product of sets A and B
$\mathfrak{D}(r)$	domain of the relation r
$\mathfrak{R}(r)$	range of the relation r
r^{-1}	inverse of the relation r
I_A	the identity relation in A
$\mathcal{P}$	partitions
$f: A \longrightarrow B$	f is a function from A to B
$f: A \xrightarrow{\text{onto}} B$	f is a function from A onto B
$f: A \xrightarrow[1-1]{} B$	f is a 1–1 function from A to B
$f: A \xrightarrow[1-1]{\text{onto}} B$	f is a 1–1 function from A onto B
$y = f(x)$	y is the image of x under the function f
$g \circ f$	the composition of g and f (where g and f are functions)
$f \mid A'$	the restriction of f to A'

$A \sim B$	set A is equivalent to set B
$\displaystyle\sum_{t \in T} \gamma_t$	sum of the cardinal numbers γ_t
F^+	the set of positive fractions
F^-	the set of negative fractions
R^+	the set of positive rational numbers
R^-	the set of negative rational numbers
$\#(A)$	cardinal number of set A
$\overline{\overline{A}}$	set of all sets equivalent to set A
α	cardinal number of the set of natural numbers
c	cardinal number of the set of real numbers
$\aleph_0$	Cantor's cardinal number for the set of natural numbers
$\beta, \gamma, \mu, \nu, \rho$	arbitrary cardinal or ordinal numbers
$[0,1]$	the set of all real numbers x such that $0 \leq x \leq 1$
$[0,1)$	the set of all real numbers x such that $0 \leq x < 1$
$<$	an arbitrary ordering relation
(A,r)	an ordered set (set A with ordering relation r in A)
$(A,r) \simeq (B,t)$	(A,r) is similar to (B,t)
$[(A,r)]$	the ordinal number of (A,r)
ω	ordinal number of $(N,<)$

BIBLIOGRAPHY

TEXTS ON SET THEORY

Breuer, Joseph, *Introduction to the Theory of Sets* (Englewood Cliffs,N. J.: Prentice-Hall, Inc., 1958).

Christian, Robert, *Introduction to Logic and Sets*, Preliminary Edition (Boston: Ginn and Company, 1958).

Committee on the Undergraduate Program, Mathematical Association of America, *Elementary Mathematics of Sets with Applications* (Ann Arbor, Michigan, 1959).

Fraenkel, Abraham, *Abstract Set Theory* (Amsterdam: Holland Publishing Company, 1961).

Halmos, Paul, *Naive Set Theory* (Princeton, N.J.: D. Van Nostrand Company, Inc., 1960).

Hamilton, Norman, and Joseph Landin, *Set Theory: the Structure of Arithmetic* (Boston: Allyn and Bacon, Inc., 1961).

Hausdorff, Felix, trans., *Set Theory* (New York: Chelsea Publishing Company, 1957).

Kamke, E., trans., *Theory of Sets* (New York: Dover Publications, Inc., 1950).

Krickenberger, W. R., and Helen Pearson, *An Introduction to Sets and the Structure of Algebra* (Boston: Ginn and Company, 1958).

Stoll, Robert R., *Sets, Logic and Axiomatic Theories* (San Francisco: W. H. Freeman and Company, 1961).

Suppes, Patrick, *Axiomatic Set Theory* (Princeton, N.J.: D. Van Nostrand Company, Inc., 1960).

Wilder, Raymond L., *The Foundations of Mathematics* (New York: John Wiley & Sons, Inc., 1958).

TEXTS ON MATHEMATICAL LOGIC

Ambrose, Alice, and Morris Lazerowitz, *Fundamentals of Symbolic Logic* (New York: Rinehart and Company, Inc., 1954).

Exner, Robert, and Myron Rosskopf, *Logic in Elementary Mathematics* (New York: McGraw-Hill Book Company, 1959).

Hilbert, D., and W. Ackerman, trans., *Principles of Mathematical Logic* (New York: Chelsea Publishing Company, 1950).

Suppes, Patrick, *Introduction to Logic* (Princeton, N.J.: D. Van Nostrand Company, Inc., 1957).

ANSWERS TO SELECTED EXERCISES

1.

p	q	$p \Rightarrow q$	$p \wedge (p \Rightarrow q)$	$p \wedge (p \Rightarrow q) \Rightarrow q$
T	T	T	T	T
T	F	F	F	T
F	T	T	F	T
F	F	T	F	T

2.

p	q	$p \wedge q$	$(p \wedge q) \Rightarrow q$
T	T	T	T
T	F	F	T
F	T	F	T
F	F	F	T

6.

p	q	$-p$	$-q$	$p \Rightarrow q$	$p \Rightarrow -q$	$p \Rightarrow q \wedge$ $p \Rightarrow -q$	$(p \Rightarrow q \wedge p \Rightarrow -q)$ $\Rightarrow -p$
T	T	F	F	T	F	F	T
T	F	F	T	F	T	F	T
F	T	T	F	T	T	T	T
F	F	T	T	T	T	T	T

15.

p	q	$-p$	$p \Rightarrow q$	$-p \vee q$	$(p \Rightarrow q) \Leftrightarrow (-p \vee q)$
T	T	F	T	T	T
T	F	F	F	F	T
F	T	T	T	T	T
F	F	T	T	T	T

. . . .

SECTION 2.1

2. $C = \{x; x \in Z, x = 2n$ for some $n \in Z\}$.

3. $B = \{-4, -3, -2, -1, 0, 1, 2, 3, 4\}$.

. . . .

SECTION 2.2

1. a. Proof: Let $x \in A$.   Then it follows that $x \in A$ (since $p \Leftrightarrow p$). Since x was chosen as an arbitrary element of A, it follows that every element of A is an element of A, and hence $A \subseteq A$ by definition of "subset."

1. c. Proof: $\forall \, x \in A, x \in B$.   (By def. of $\subseteq$)

$\qquad\qquad \forall \, x \in B, x \in C$.   (By def. of $\subseteq$)

Thus, $\forall \, x \in A, x \in C$. $(p \Rightarrow q) \wedge (q \Rightarrow r) \Rightarrow (p \Rightarrow r)$

Therefore, $A \subseteq C$.   (By def. of $\subseteq$)

Since, $B \subset C, \exists \, x \in C \ni x \notin B$.   (By def. of $\subset$)

But $x \notin B$ implies $x \notin A$, for otherwise $A \not\subseteq B$ which contradicts the hypothesis.

Therefore, $\exists \, x \in C \ni x \notin A$, and we have $A \subset C$.

$\qquad\qquad\qquad\qquad\qquad\qquad\qquad\qquad\qquad$ (By def. of $\subset$)

3. Proof: If $A \subseteq \varnothing$, then since $\varnothing \subseteq A$ (Theorem 2.1), we have $A = \varnothing$ (Theorem 2.2).

If $A = \emptyset$, then it follows that $A \subseteq \emptyset$ and $\emptyset \subseteq A$ (Theorem 2.2). Therefore, $A \subseteq \emptyset$ $(p \wedge q \Rightarrow p)$.

Since $(A \subseteq \emptyset) \Rightarrow (A = \emptyset)$ and $(A = \emptyset) \Rightarrow (A \subseteq \emptyset)$, $(A \subseteq \emptyset) \Leftrightarrow (A = \emptyset)$ (Table 1.6).

4. Let $A = \{1,2\}$ and $B = \{\{1,2\}, \{3,4\}, \{a,b\}\}$. Then $A \in B$.
Let $A = \{a,b\}$ and $B = \{a,b,c,d\}$. Then $A \subset B$.
Let $A = \{a,b\}$ and $B = \{a,b\}$. Then $A = B$.

6. The number elements (sets) in $p(A)$ is 2^n.

. . . .

SECTION 2.3

1. Proof: Let $x \in (A - B)$. Then $x \in A$ and $x \notin B$ by Def. 2.7. Thus, $x \in A$ by Exercise 1.5–2. Since x was arbitrarily chosen, every element of $A - B$ is an element of A. Hence, $(A - B) \subseteq A$ by Def. 2.1.

3. Proof: Let $x \in A - (A - \emptyset)$. Then $x \in A$ and $x \notin (A - \emptyset)$. Now $x \notin (A - \emptyset)$ implies $x \notin A$ or $x \in \emptyset$. Thus $(x \in A) \wedge (x \notin A \vee x \in \emptyset)$, from which it follows that $(x \in A \wedge x \notin A) \vee (x \in A \wedge x \in \emptyset)$. Hence, we must have $x \in \emptyset$, for $(x \in A \wedge x \notin A) \Rightarrow x \in \emptyset$ and $(x \in A \wedge x \in \emptyset) \Rightarrow x \in \emptyset$. Since x was an arbitrary element of $A - (A - \emptyset)$, we see that every element of $A - (A - \emptyset)$ is an element of $\emptyset$. Therefore, $A - (A - \emptyset) \subseteq \emptyset$.

Since $\emptyset \subseteq A - (A - \emptyset)$, by Theorem 2.1, we conclude that $A - (A - \emptyset) = \emptyset$ from Theorem 2.2.

7. Let $A = \{1,2,3\}$ and $B = \{1,2,3,4\}$. Then $A - B = \emptyset$ and $B - A = \{4\}$. Since $\emptyset \neq \{4\}$, in this case $A - B \neq B - A$. Therefore, in general $A - B \neq B - A$, for there exist sets A and B such that $A - B \neq B - A$.

. . . .

SECTION 2.4

3. Proof: Let $x \in A \cap B$. Then $x \in A$ and $x \in B$ by Def. 2.10. But $p \wedge q \Rightarrow p$, therefore, $x \in A \wedge x \in B \Rightarrow x \in A$. Finally,

$x \in A \Rightarrow (x \in A \vee x \in B)$, since $p \Rightarrow p \vee q$. Thus, $x \in A \cup B$ by Def. 2.8. Since x was chosen arbitrarily, $A \cap B \subseteq A \cup B$ by Def. 2.1.

4. a. $\{w,x,y,z\}$.
   b. $\{y\}$.

. . . .

SECTION 2.6

4. Proof: Let $x \in C - (A \cap B)$. Then $x \in C$ and $x \notin (A \cap B)$ (definition of complement). But $x \notin (A \cap B) \Rightarrow (x \notin A$ or $x \notin B)$ $(-(p \wedge q) \Rightarrow (-p \vee -q))$, thus, $x \in C \wedge (x \notin A \vee x \notin B)$, and hence $(x \in C \wedge x \notin A) \vee (x \in C \wedge x \notin B)$ (see Exercise 1.5–14).

Therefore, $x \in (C - A) \cup (C - B)$ (definitions of complement and union). We conclude that $C - (A \cap B) \subseteq (C - A) \cup (C - B)$.

Since the steps above are completely reversible, $(C - A) \cup (C - B) \subseteq C - (A \cap B)$. Therefore, $C - (A \cap B) = (C - A) \cup (C - B)$ (Theorem 2.2).

12. Proof: Let $x \in A \cap B$. Then $x \in A$ and $x \in B$ by definition of intersection. But $x \in B \Rightarrow x \in C$ since $B \subseteq C$. Thus, $x \in A$ and $x \in C$ or, by definition of intersection, $x \in A \cap C$. Therefore, $A \cap B \subseteq A \cap C$ by definition of subset.

17. Proof: (several tautologies are needed in the following, and the reader is asked to supply those needed.)
$x \in (A - B) \cup (B - A) \Rightarrow (x \in A - B \vee x \in B - A)$
$\Rightarrow (x \in A \wedge x \notin B) \vee (x \in B \wedge x \notin A)$
$\Rightarrow [(x \in A \wedge x \notin B) \vee x \in B] \wedge [(x \in A \wedge x \notin B) \vee x \notin A]$
$\Rightarrow [(x \in B \vee x \in A) \wedge (x \in B \vee x \notin B)] \wedge [(x \notin A \vee x \in A) \wedge (x \notin B \vee x \notin A)]$
$\Rightarrow (x \in B \cup A) \wedge (x \notin B \cap A)$
$\Rightarrow [x \in (B \cup A) - (B \cap A)]$
$\Rightarrow (A - B) \cup (B - A) \subseteq (A \cup B) - (A \cap B)$.

The proof showing the inclusion $(A \cup B) - (A \cap B) \subseteq (A - B) \cup (B - A)$ is similar to that above, and we conclude the equality from Theorem 2.2.

. . . .

SECTION 3.2

2. Proof: Assume $a = b$. Then $\{a,b\} = \{a\}$, and since $\{a\} = \{a\}$, it follows that $\{\{a\}, \{a,b\}\} = \{\{a\}, \{a\}\} = \{\{a\}\}$ by the Axiom of Extent.

Assume $\{\{a\}, \{a,b\}\} = \{\{a\}\}$. Then $\{a\} = \{a\}$ and $\{a,b\} = \{a\}$ by the Axiom of Extent. With $\{a,b\} = \{a\}$ we have $b = a$, again by the Axiom of Extent.

Therefore, we obtain the result desired by Exercise 1.5–8.

. . . .

SECTION 3.3

2. e.

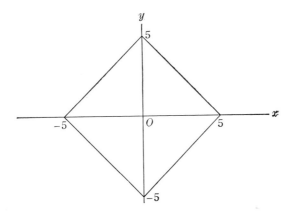

2. f.

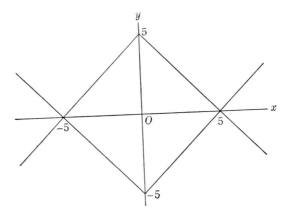

3. Proof: Let (a,c) be an arbitrary element of $A \times C$. Then $a \in A$ and $c \in C$. It follows that $a \in B$ since $A \subseteq B$. Therefore, $(a,c) \in B \times C$. Hence, $A \times C \subseteq B \times C$.

5. Proof: Let $(x,y) \in A \times (B \cap C)$. Then $x \in A$ and $y \in B \cap C$. Thus, $x \in A \wedge (y \in B \wedge y \in C)$. Hence, $(x \in A \wedge y \in B) \wedge (x \in A \wedge y \in C)$. Therefore, $(x,y) \in A \times B$ and $(x,y) \in A \times C$ or $(x,y) \in A \times B \cap A \times C$; thus, $A \times (B \cap C) \subseteq A \times B \cap A \times C$.

Since the above steps are reversible, we may conclude that $A \times B \cap A \times C \subseteq A \times (B \cap C)$ and hence $A \times (B \cap C) = A \times B \cap A \times C$.

. . . .

SECTION 3.4

2. First, $x^2 + y^2 + 2x = 4y - 6$ is equivalent to $(x + 1)^2 + (y - 2)^2 = -1$. Since x and y are real numbers, $(x + 1)^2 \geq 0$ and $(y - 2)^2 \geq 0$. Therefore, there exist no real numbers x and y such that $(x + 1)^2 + (y - 2)^2 = -1$.

Since r is empty, $\mathcal{D}(r) = \emptyset$ and $\mathcal{R}(r) = \emptyset$. Let $A = C$ (complex numbers) and $B = Z$ (the integers). Then r is a non-empty relation from A to B, for $(-1 + i, 2)$ is an element of this new relation.

4. (i) Proof: Let $y \in \mathcal{D}(r^{-1})$. Then $y \in B$, and there exists $x \in A$ such that $(y,x) \in r^{-1}$. But then $(x,y) \in r$, and we have $y \in \mathcal{R}(r)$. Thus, $\mathcal{D}(r^{-1}) \subseteq \mathcal{R}(r)$. Similarly, $\mathcal{R}(r) \subseteq \mathcal{D}(r^{-1})$, and we conclude that $\mathcal{D}(r^{-1}) = \mathcal{R}(r)$.

6. (1) $r_1 = \{(0,0), (1,1), (2,2), (3,3), (4,4), (1,3), (3,2)\}$.
   (4) $r_4 = \{(0,0), (1,1), (2,2), (3,3), (4,4), (2,4), (4,2), (3,2), (2,3)\}$.
   (8) $r_8 = \{(0,0), (1,1), (4,3), (3,2)\}$.

10. Proof: (i) For each $a \in A$, $(a,a) \in r$ since r is reflexive. Therefore, $(a,a) \in r^{-1}$. Hence, r^{-1} is reflexive.

(ii) If $(a,b) \in r^{-1}$, then $(b,a) \in r$. Since r is symmetric, $(a,b) \in r$. But then $(b,a) \in r^{-1}$, and it follows that r^{-1} is symmetric.

(iii) If $(a,b) \in r^{-1}$ and $(b,c) \in r^{-1}$, then (c,b) and (b,a) are elements of r. But r is transitive, so $(c,a) \in r$. Hence, $(a,c) \in r^{-1}$, and r^{-1} is transitive.

Since r^{-1} is reflexive, symmetric and transitive, it follows that r^{-1} is an equivalence relation whenever r is an equivalence relation.

. . . .

SECTION 3.5

1. Proof: For each $x \in Z$, $x - x = 0 = 3 \cdot 0$ where $0 \in Z$. Therefore, $(x,x) \in r$ by definition of r, and r is reflexive.

If $(x,y) \in r$, then $x - y = 3n$ for some $n \in Z$. Hence, $y - x = 3(-n)$ where $-n \in Z$ and $(y,x) \in r$ by definition of r. Thus, r is symmetric.

If $(x,y) \in r$ and $(y,z) \in r$, then $x - y = 3n_1$ for some $n_1 \in Z$ and $y - z = 3n_2$ for some $n_2 \in Z$.

It follows that $x - z = 3(n_1 + n_2)$ where $(n_1 + n_2) \in Z$. Therefore, $(x,z) \in r$ by definition of r. We may conclude that r is transitive.

Since r is reflexive, symmetric and transitive, r is an equivalence relation by definition.

. . . .

SECTION 3.6

1. a. f is not a function since $\mathfrak{D}(f) \neq A$.
   c. h is not a function since $(1,e) \in h$ and $(1,d) \in h$, and we assume $e \neq d$.
   e. k is a function whose range is B.

3. Proof: I_A is a relation by definition. Further, for each $x \in A$, $(x,x) \in I_A$ by definition of I_A so $\mathfrak{D}(I_A) = A$. Finally, if $(x,y) \in I_A$ and $(x,z) \in I_A$, then $x = y$ and $x = z$ by definition of I_A. Therefore, $y = z$ and I_A is a function.

. . . .

SECTION 3.7

3. a. Not a function.

   c. 1–1 and onto function.

   d. A function but not 1–1 and not onto.

5. a. f is a function but not onto although 1–1.

     Proof: Clearly f is a relation in Z. Also, $\forall\, x \in Z, \exists\, y \in Z$, namely $y = 2x$, such that $(x,y) \in f$. Thus, $\mathfrak{D}(f) = Z$. Moreover, if $(x,y) \in f$ and $(x,z) \in f$, then $y = 2x = z$. Therefore, f is a function.

     f is not onto Z, since $3 \in Z$ and there does not exist an integer x such that $3 = 2x$.

     f is 1–1, for if $(x,y) \in f$ and $(z,y) \in f$, then $y = 2x$ and $y = 2z$, from which it follows that $x = z$.

. . . .

SECTION 3.8

2. Proof: Clearly $*$ is a relation from $Z \times Z$ to Z. Furthermore, for each $(x,y) \in Z \times Z$, there exists $z \in Z$, namely $z = x + y - 1$, such that $((x,y),z) \in *$. Thus, $\mathfrak{D}(*) = Z \times Z$. Now if $((x,y),z_1) \in *$ and $((x,y),z_2) \in *$, then $z_1 = x + y - 1 = z_2$, and it follows that $*$ is a function and therefore a binary operation.

3. Proof: Since $9 = 7 + 3 - 1$ and $9 = 3 + 7 - 1$, it follows that $((7,3),9) \in *$ and $((3,7),9) \in *$. With the fact that $(7,3) \neq (3,7)$, we can conclude that $*$ is not 1–1.

. . . .

SECTION 3.9

1. Proof: Let z be an arbitrary element of C. Since g is a function from B onto C, it follows that there exists $y \in B$ such that $(y,z) \in g$. Also, since f is a function from A onto B, there exists $x \in A$ such that $(x,y) \in f$. Therefore, since $g(f(x)) = z$, $(x,z) \in g \circ f$. Hence $z \in \mathfrak{R}(g \circ f)$ and $C \subseteq \mathfrak{R}(g \circ f)$. Thus, with $\mathfrak{R}(g \circ f) \subseteq C$, we have $\mathfrak{R}(g \circ f) = C$, and $g \circ f$ is onto.

     Let $(x_1,z) \in g \circ f$ and $(x_2,z) \in g \circ f$. Then, $\exists\, y_1, y_2 \in B \ni$

$(x_1,y_1) \in f$, $(y_1,z) \in g$, $(x_2,y_2) \in f$ and $(y_2,z) \in g$. But $(y_1,z) \in g$ and $(y_2,z) \in g \Rightarrow y_1 = y_2$ since g is 1–1. If $(x_1,y_1) \in f$ and $(x_2,y_1) \in f$, then $x_1 = x_2$ since f is 1–1. Therefore, $g \circ f$ is 1–1.

6. a. $(E,+)$ is a group by definition.

   b. $(E,\cdot)$ is not a group since there is no "zero" element for this operation.

   e. $(D,\cdot)$ is not a group since there is no odd integer which, when multiplied by 5, gives 1.

. . . .

SECTION 3.10

1. Proof: Let $x \in A'$. Then $x \in A$ since $A' \subseteq A$. But then $\exists \, y \in B$ such that $(x,y) \in f$. Therefore, $(x,y) \in f \mid A'$, and hence $A' \subseteq \mathcal{D}(f \mid A')$. By definition, $\mathcal{D}(f \mid A') \subseteq A'$, and it follows that $\mathcal{D}(f \mid A') = A'$.

   If (x,y) and (x,z) are elements of $f \mid A'$, then (x,y) and (x,z) are elements of f by definition of $f \mid A'$. Therefore $y = z$ since f is a function, and $f \mid A'$ is a function from A' to B.

. . . .

SECTION 4.2

2. 120

3. $k!$

INDEX